TWO ADOLESCENTS

Only once did his mother seem aware of his presence, and that was when the young man, letting go the oars for a moment, leaned forward with an intensely malicious expression on his face and murmured something in an undertone which Agostino could not. understand. His mother started, pretending to be terribly shocked, and cried out, pointing to Agostino sitting by her, "Let us at least spare this innocent!" Agostino trembled with rage at hearing himself called innocent, as if a dirty rag had been thrown at him which he could not avoid.—from AGOSTINO

But then, as he touched the dimple in her chin, he suddenly realized that a second game had taken the place of the first; and this second game was not really a game at all, but the usual hankering that impelled him every day to leave his table and look into the sitting room. At this thought, a feeling of strong excitement took his breath away and made his face burn.—from LUCA

Alberto Moravia is widely recognized as Italy's greatest contemporary novelist. In TWO ADOLESCENTS he brilliantly explores the complex transition, from boyhood to manhood, of two youths whose lives are totally different.

"One of the best writers in the world today."
TIME MAGAZINE

Also by Alberto Moravia

FICTION

The Woman of Rome
The Conformist
Time of Desecration
The Fancy Dress Party
The Time of Indifference
Conjugal Love
Roman Tales
A Ghost at Noon
Bitter Honeymoon
Two Women
The Wayward Wife
The Empty Canvas
More Roman Tales
The Fetish
The Lie
Command and I Will Obey You
Paradise
The Two of Us
Lady Godiva
The Voice of the Sea

GENERAL

Man as an End
The Red Book and the Great Wall
Which Tribe Do You Belong To?

PLAY

Beatrice Cenci

ALBERTO MORAVIA

TWO ADOLESCENTS

TWO ADOLESCENTS

Published in the United States by Playboy Paperbacks, New York, New York. Printed in the United States of America. Library of Congress Catalog Card Number: 81-82970. Reprinted by arrangement with Farrar, Straus & Giroux.

Books are available at quantity discounts for promotional and industrial use. For further information, write to Premium Sales, Playboy Paperbacks, 1633 Broadway, New York, New York 10019.

ISBN: 0-867-21001-X

First Playboy Paperbacks printing February 1982.

AGOSTINO

Translated from the Italian
by Beryl de Zoete

During those days of early summer Agostino and his mother used to go out every morning on a bathing raft. The first few times his mother had taken a boatman, but Agostino so plainly showed his annoyance at the man's presence that from then on the oars were entrusted to him. It gave him intense pleasure to row on that calm, transparent, early morning sea; and his mother sat facing him, as gay and serene as the sea and sky, and talked to him in a soft voice, just as if he had been a man instead of a thirteen-year-old boy. Agostino's mother was a tall, beautiful woman, still in her prime, and Agostino felt a sense of pride each time he set out with her on one of those morning expeditions. It seemed to him that all the bathers on the beach were watching them, admiring his mother and envying him. In the conviction that all eyes were upon them his voice sounded to him stronger than usual, and he felt as if all his movements had something symbolic about them, as if they were part of a play; as if he and his mother, instead of being on the beach, were on a stage, under the eager eyes of hundreds of spectators. Sometimes his mother would appear in a new dress, and he could not resist remarking on it aloud, in the secret hope that others would hear. Now and again she would send him to fetch something or other from the beach cabin, while she stood waiting for him by the boat. He would obey with a secret joy, happy if he could prolong their departure even by a few minutes. At last they would get on the raft, and Agostino would take the oars and row out to sea. But for quite a long time he would remain under the disturbing influence of his filial vanity. When they were some way from the shore his mother would tell him to stop rowing, put on her rubber bathing cap, take off her sandals and slip into the water. Agostino would follow her. They swam round and round the empty raft with its floating oars, talking gaily together, their voices ringing clear in the silence of the calm, sunlit sea. Sometimes his mother would point to a piece of cork bobbing up and down a short distance from them, and challenge him to race her to it. She gave him a few yards start, and they would swim as hard as they could toward the cork. Or they would have diving competitions from the platform of the raft, splashing up the pale, smooth water as they plunged in. Agostino would watch his mother's body sink down deeper and deeper through a froth of green bubbles; then suddenly he would dive in after her, eager to follow wherever she might go, even to the bottom of the sea. As he flung himself into the furrow his mother had made it seemed to him that even that cold, dense water must keep some trace of the passage of her beloved body. When their swim was over they would climb back onto the raft, and gazing all round her on the calm, luminous sea his mother would say: "How beautiful it is, isn't it?" Agostino made no reply, because he felt that his own enjoyment of the beauty of sea and sky was really due above all to his deep sense of union with his mother. Were it not for this intimacy, it sometimes entered his head to wonder what would remain of all that beauty. They would stay out a long time, drying themselves in the sun, which toward midday got hotter and hotter; then his mother, stretched out at full length on the platform between the two floats, with her long hair trailing in the water and her eyes closed, would fall into a doze, while Agostino would keep watch from his seat on the bench, his eyes fixed on his mother, and hardly breathing for fear of disturbing her slumber. Suddenly she would open her eyes and say what a delightful novelty it was to lie on one's back with one's eyes shut and to feel the water rocking underneath; or she would ask Agostino to pass her her cigarette case or, better still, to light one for her himself and give it to her. All of which he would do with fervent and tremulous care. While his mother smoked, Agostino would lean forward with his back to her, but with his head on one side so that he could watch the clouds of blue smoke which indicated the spot where his mother's head was resting, with her hair spread out round her on the water. Then, as she never could have enough of the sun, she would ask Agostino to row on and not turn round, while she would take off her brassière and let down her bathing suit so as to expose her whole body to the sunlight. Agostino would go on rowing, proud of her injunction not to look as if he were being allowed to take part in a ritual. And not only did he never dream of looking around, but he felt that her body, lying so close behind him, naked in the sun, was surrounded by a halo of mystery to which he owed the greatest reverence.

One morning his mother was sitting as usual under the great beach umbrella, with Agostino beside her on the sand, waiting for the moment of their daily row. Suddenly a tall shadow fell between him and the sun. He looked up and saw a dark, sunburnt young man shaking hands with his mother. He did not pay much attention to him, thinking it was one of his mother's casual acquaintances; he only drew back a little, waiting for the conversation to be over. But the young man did not accept the invitation to sit down; pointing to the white raft in which he had come, he invited the mother to go for a row. Agostino was sure his mother would refuse this invitation as she had many previous ones; so that his surprise was great when he saw her accept at once, and immediately begin to put her things together—her sandals, bathing cap and purse, and then get up from her chair. His mother had accepted the young man's invitation with exactly the same spontaneity and simple friendliness which she would have have shown toward her son; and with a like simplicity she now turned to Agostino, who sat waiting with his head down, letting the sand trickle through his fingers, and told him to have a sun bath, for she was going out for a short turn in the boat and would be back soon. The young man, meanwhile, as if quite sure of himself, had gone off in the direction of the raft, while the woman walked submissively behind him with her usual calm, majestic gait. Her son, watching them, could not help saying to himself that the young man must now be feeling the same pride and vanity and excitement which he himself always felt when he set out in a boat with his mother. He watched her get onto the float: the young man leaned backward and pushed with his feet against the sandy bottom; then, with a few vigorous strokes, lifted the raft out of the shallow water near the shore. The young man was rowing now, and his mother sat facing him, holding onto the seat with both hands and apparently chatting with him. Gradually the raft grew smaller and smaller, till it entered the region of dazzling light which the sun shed on the surface of the water, and slowly became absorbed into it.

Left alone, Agostino stretched himself out in his mother's deck chair and with one arm behind his head lay gazing up at the sky, seemingly lost in reflection and indifferent to his surroundings. He felt that all the people on the beach must have noticed him going off every day with his mother, and therefore it could not have escaped them that today his mother had left him behind and gone off with the young man of the bathing raft. So he was determined to give no sign at all of the disappointment and disillusion which filled him with such bitterness. But however much he tried to adopt an air of calm composure, he felt at the same time that everyone must be noticing how forced and artificial his attitude was. What hurt him still more was not so much that his mother had preferred the young man's company to his as the alacrity with which she had accepted the invitation—almost as if she had anticipated it. It was as if she had decided beforehand not to lose any opportunity, and when one offered itself to accept it without hesitation. Apparently she had been bored all those times she had been alone with him on the raft, and had only gone with him for lack of something better to do. A memory came back to his mind that increased his discomfiture. It had happened at a dance to which he had been taken by his mother. A girl cousin was with them who, in despair at not being asked by anyone else, had consented to dance once or twice with him, though he was only a boy in short trousers. She had danced reluctantly and looked very cross and out of temper, and Agostino, though preoccupied with his own steps, was aware of her contemptuous and unflattering sentiments toward himself. He had, however, asked her for a third dance, and had been quite surprised to see her suddenly smile and leap from her chair, shaking out the folds of her dress with both hands. But instead of rushing into his arms she had turned her back on him and joined a young man who had motioned to her over Agostino's shoulder. The whole scene lasted only five seconds, and no one noticed anything except Agostino himself. But he felt utterly humiliated and was sure everyone had seen how he had been snubbed.

And now, after his mother had gone off with the young man, he compared the two happenings and found them identical. Like his cousin, his mother had only waited for an opportunity to abandon him. Like his cousin, and with the same exaggerated readiness, she had accepted the first offer that presented itself. And in each case it had been his fate to come tumbling down from an illusory height and to lie bruised and wounded at the bottom.

That day his mother stayed out for about two hours. From under his big umbrella he saw her step on to the shore, shake hands with the young man and move slowly off toward the beach cabin, stooping a little under the heat of the midday sun. The beach was deserted by now, and this was a relief to Agostino, who was always convinced that all eyes were fixed on them. "What have you been doing?" his mother asked casually. "I have had great fun," began Agostino, and he made up a story of how *he* had been bathing too with the boys from the next beach cabin. But his mother was not listening; she had hurried off to dress. Agostino decided that as soon as he saw the raft appear the next day he would make some excuse to leave so as not to suffer the indignity of being left behind again. But when the next day came he had just started away when he heard his mother calling him back. "Come along," she said, as she got up and collected her belongings, "we're going out to swim." Agostino followed her, thinking that she meant to dismiss the young man and go out alone with him. The young man was standing on the raft waiting for her. She greeted him and said simply: "I'm bringing my son, too." So Agostino, much as he disliked it, found himself sitting beside his mother facing the young man, who was rowing.

Agostino had always seen his mother in a certain light—calm, dignified and reserved. During this outing he was shocked to see the change which had taken place, not only in her manner of talking but, as it seemed, even in herself. One could scarcely believe she was the same person. They had hardly put out to sea before she made some stinging personal remark, quite lost on Agostino, which started a curious, private conversation. As far as he could make out it concerned a lady friend of the young man who had rejected his advances in favor of a rival. But this only led up to the real matter of their conversation, which seemed to be alternately insinuating, exacting, contemptuous and teasing. His mother appeared to be the more aggressive and the more susceptible of the two, for the young man contented himself with replying in a calm, ironical tone, as if he were quite sure of himself. At times his mother seemed displeased, even positively angry with the young man, and then Agostino was glad. But immediately after she would disappoint him by some flattering phrase which destroyed the illusion. Or in an offended voice she would address to the young man a string of mysterious reproaches. But instead of being offended, Agostino would see his face light up with an expression of fatuous vanity, and concluded that those reproaches were only a cover for some affectionate meaning which he was unable to fathom. As for himself, both his mother and the young man seemed to be unaware of his existence; he might as well not have been there, and his mother carried this obliviousness so far as to remind the young man that if she had gone out alone with him the day before, this was a mistake on her part which she did not intend to repeat. In the future she would bring her son with her. Agostino felt this to be decidedly insulting, as if he was something with no will of its own, merely an object to be disposed of as her caprice or convenience might see fit.

Only once did his mother seem aware of his presence, and that was when the young man, letting go the oars for a moment, leaned forward with an intensely malicious expression on his face and murmured something in an undertone which Agostino could not understand. His mother started, pretending to be terribly shocked, and cried out, pointing to Agostino sitting by her, "Let us at least spare this innocent!" Agostino trembled with rage at hearing himself called innocent, as if a dirty rag had been thrown at him which he could not avoid.

When they were some way out from shore, the young man suggested a swim to his companion. Agostino, who had often admired the ease and simplicity with which his mother slipped into the water, was painfully struck by all the unfamiliar movements she now put into that familiar action. The young man had time to dive in and come up again to the surface, while she still stood hesitating and dipping one toe after another into the water, apparently pretending to be timid or shy. She made a great fuss about going in, laughing and protesting and holding on to the seat with both hands, till at last she dropped in an almost indecent attitude over the side and let herself fall clumsily into the arms of her companion. They dived together and came up together to the surface. Agostino, huddled on the seat, saw his mother's smiling face quite close to the young man's grave, brown one, and it seemed to him that their cheeks touched. He could see their two bodies disporting themselves in the limpid water, their hips and legs touching, and looking as if they longed to interlace with each other. Agostino looked first at them and then at the distant shore, with a shameful sense of being in the way. Catching sight of his frowning face, his mother, who was having her second dip, called up to him: "Why are you so serious? Don't you see how lovely it is in here? Goodness! what a serious son I've got"; a remark which filled Agostino with a sense of shame and humiliation. He made no reply, and contented himself with looking elsewhere. The swim was a long one. His mother and her companion disported themselves in the water like two dolphins, and seemed to have forgotten him entirely. At last they got back onto the raft. The young man sprang on at one bound, and then leaned over the edge to assist his companion, who was calling him to help her get out of the water. Agostino saw how in raising her the young man gripped her brown flesh with his fingers, just where the arm is softest and biggest, between the shoulder and the armpit. Then she sat down beside Agostino, panting and laughing, and with her pointed nails held her wet suit away from her, so that it should not cling to her breasts. Agostino remembered that when they were alone his mother was strong enough to climb into the boat without anyone's aid, and attributed her appeal for help and her bodily postures, which seemed to draw attention to her feminine disabilities, to the new spirit which had already produced such unpleasant changes in her. Indeed, he could not help thinking that his mother, who was naturally a tall, dignified woman, resented her size as a positive drawback from which she would have liked to rid herself; and her dignity as a tiresome habit which she was trying to replace by a sort of tomboy gaucherie.

When they were both back on the raft, the return journey began. This time the oars were entrusted to Agostino, while the other two sat down on the platform which joined the two floats. He rowed gently in the burning sun, wondering constantly about the meaning of the sounds and laughter and movements of which he was conscious behind his back. From time to time his mother, as if suddenly aware of his presence, would reach up with one arm and try to stroke the back of his neck, or she would tickle him under the arm and ask if he were tired. "No, I am not tired," he replied. He heard the young man say laughingly: "Rowing's good for him," which made him plunge in the oar savagely. His mother was sitting with her head resting against his seat and her long legs stretched out; that he knew, but it seemed to him that she did not stay in that position; once, for instance, a short skirmish seemed to be going on; his mother made a stifled sound as if she were being suffocated and the raft lurched to one side. For a moment Agostino's cheek came into contact with his mother's body, which seemed vast to him—like the sky—and pulsing with a life over which she had no control. She stood with her legs apart, holding on to her son's shoulders, and said: "I will only sit down again if you promise to be good." "I promise," rejoined the young man with mock solemnity. She let herself down again awkwardly on to the platform, and it was then her body brushed her son's cheek. The moisture of her body confined in its wet bathing suit remained on his skin, but its heat seemed to overpower its dampness and though he felt a tormenting sense of uneasiness, even of repugnance, he persisted in not drying away the traces.

As they approached the shore the young man sprang lightly to the rower's seat and seized the oars, pushing Agostino away and forcing him to take the place left empty beside his mother. She put her arm round his waist and asked how he felt, and if he was happy. She herself seemed in the highest spirits, and began singing, another most unusual thing with her. She had a sweet voice, and put in some pathetic trills which made Agostino shiver. While she sang she continued to hold him close to her, wetting him with the water from her damp bathing suit, which seemed to exude a violent animal heat. And so they came in to the shore, the young man rowing, the woman singing and caressing her son, who submitted with a feeling of utter boredom; making up a picture which Agostino felt to be false, and contrived for appearance's sake.

Next day the young man appeared again. Agostino's mother insisted on her son coming and the scenes of the day before repeated themselves. Then after a few days' interval they went out again. And at last, with their apparently growing intimacy, he came to fetch her daily, and each time Agostino was obliged to go too, to listen to their conversation and to watch them bathing. He hated these expeditions, and invented a thousand reasons for not going. He would disappear and not show himself till his mother, having called him repeatedly and hunted for him everywhere, succeeded at last in unearthing him; but then he came less in response to her appeals than because her disappointment and vexation aroused his pity. He kept completely silent on the float, hoping they would understand and leave him alone, but in the end he proved weaker and more susceptible to pity than his mother or the young man. It was enough for them just to have him there; as for his feelings, he came to see that they counted for less than nothing. So, in spite of all his attempts to escape, the expeditions continued.

One day Agostino was sitting on the sand behind his mother's deck chair, waiting for the white raft to appear on the sea and for his mother to wave her hand in greeting and call to the young man by name. But the usual hour for his appearance passed, and his mother's disappointed and cross expression clearly showed that she had given up all hope of his coming. Agostino had often wondered what he should feel in such a case, and had supposed that his joy would have been at least as great as his mother's disappointment. But he was surprised to feel instead a vague disappointment, and he realized that the humiliations and resentments of those daily outings had become almost a necessity of life to him. Therefore, with a confused and unconscious desire to inflict pain on his mother, he asked her more than once if they were not going out for their usual row. She replied each time that she didn't know, but that probably they wouldn't be going today. She lay in the deck chair with a book open in her lap, but she wasn't reading and her eyes continually wandered out to sea, as if seeking some particular object among the many boats and bathers with which the water was already swarming. After sitting a long time behind his mother's chair, drawing patterns in the sand, Agostino came round to her and said in a tone of voice which he felt to be teasing and even mocking: "Mamma, do you mean to say that we're not going out on the raft today?" His mother may have felt the mockery in his voice and the desire to make her suffer, or his few rash words may have sufficed to release her long pent-up irritation. She raised her hand not this power exceed all creaturely capabilities? Indeed, one might almost say anxiously: Are we not transgressing the limits between God and creature and making you a sort of god, as Protestantism accuses us of doing?"

The teaching of the Church gives us a clear answer to this question: Mary is so great because she was selected to become the mother of God. And this reality exalts her infinitely above all other creatures. From this mission of hers comes all the other privileges: her perpetual virginity, her immaculate conception, her assumption into heaven. Mary has such a great role to play in the life of the Church and of every individual because, as divine revelation teaches us, God willed it so and not otherwise, although he would have had a thousand other ways of redeeming us. Saint Louis Marie de Montfort, too, explains why Mary manifests all her might and glory at the end of the ages: because the salvation of the world began through Mary, and through her it will also be brought to completion.

All these sublime truths help us not only to know and love her better and better, but also to see ever more clearly our own mission in life, which she herself essentially formulated at Fatima in those simple words: "Pray and make sacrifices, for so many souls go to hell because there is no one to pray for them and to make sacrifices for them."[3]

We can say, therefore, that the more deeply someone penetrates into the mystery of Mary, the more he becomes inflamed with love for her, and the more he sees God's mighty deeds in her, the better he comes to know God's nature. Above all, however, he also lives then more in accordance with God's will and receives from this contemplative love the strength to live out his calling.

3. *Sr. Lucia Speaks about Fatima*, 5. Auflage, (Fatima, 1987) [henceforth SLF], p. 177.

For this reason the saints could never praise Mary enough, meditate sufficiently on her glories, or fully investigate the meaning of her nature and her mission theologically. Saint Maximilian Kolbe wanted the Cities of the Immaculata to become universities and Marian academies that continually elaborate the Church's teaching on Mary's greatness, for the greater glory of God and for the greatest possible benefit for souls.

This book is an attempt to provide an overview of the doctrines of Saint Louis Marie de Montfort and Saint Maximilian Kolbe and of the apparitions of Mary, especially at Fatima, and to examine them in the light of the teaching of the popes and of the fathers of the Church. By means of these instruments which she has chosen, the Immaculata wants to let us have a glimpse into the ardent depths of her heart, into that furnace of love, into her inmost mystery. Only in this light will we then understand why she has such a momentous place in the work of redemption and what "great things" have been done in her by the Lord "who is mighty… and holy is his name!"

All the Marian saints assure us that anchoring oneself in this way in the depths of the mystery of Mary brings forth the most splendid spiritual fruits, as Saint Bernard puts it:

> O whoever you are, since you see that you are drifting along the stream of time amidst storms and tempests rather than walking upon solid ground, so to speak, do not turn your glance from this shining star, if you do not want to perish in the storms. When the storm winds of temptations arise, when you are heading for the cliffs of anxieties, look up to the star and call on Mary. When you are being swept along by the waves of arrogance or ambition, or of slander or jealousy, look up to the star and call on Mary. When anger,

> greed or the pleasures of the flesh threaten to capsize the little ship of your soul, look up to Mary. When you are confused by the terrible extent of your guilt, ashamed of the stains on your conscience, horrified by the fear of judgment and are in danger of sinking into the pit of sadness, into the abyss of despair, then think of Mary. In dangers and anxieties, in doubt and need, think of Mary, call on Mary. Let her never leave your lips, let her never depart from your heart. And in order to obtain an answer to your prayers, do not cease to imitate her life. Following her, you shall not stray; invoking her, you shall not despair; thinking of her, you shall not wander. Upheld by her, you shall not fall; shielded by her, you have nothing more to fear; guided by her, you grow not weary; favored by her, you reach the goal.[4]

But all this should not be just a sublime meditation on the most beautiful of all the flowers in God's garden; rather, our path to God consists precisely in this process of entering into her. She is in fact our deliverance, our rise from the Fall, our perseverance in battle, strength in our weakness, and finally our victory. Haven't we already experienced it so often, that when we have been faithful to Mary, our spiritual life is permeated with a comforting harmony and we receive spiritual strength that was previously unknown to us? Every one of us has to say with tears of gratitude: "I owe you my conversion, my baptism, my vocation, and everything great and genuine in my life. You have obtained these graces for me!" Now Saint Maximilian Kolbe calls to us to be consistent in following this path with her. The marvels that Mary works in the world and in souls, in my soul, too, are there ultimately so as to show me more clearly the way on which I must walk in these perilous times, when the

4. *Homilia 2 super "Missus est"*, in: *St. Bernard et Notre Dame* (Bourges, 1953), pp. 114-117.

enemy is almost overwhelming us. Entering ever more deeply into the mystery of Mary is the solution that God gives to the few who remain faithful in the end times. Thus it was clearly stated in Fatima: The mother of God gave me to understand that God is giving the world the final means of salvation, the rosary and devotion to the Immaculate Heart. But if these are the final ones, then are no more besides them.[5] Saint Louis Marie de Montfort and Saint Maximilian Kolbe explain to us the most profound elements of this devotion to the heart of the Immaculata and guide us in living it out more and more. But when Mary declares that in the end her Immaculate Heart will triumph, then anyone who lives in that heart will win the victory as well, but especially the person who lives most profoundly in that heart. These lines have been written so that this might happen.

5. J.M. Alonso, CMF, *La Verdad sobre el Secreto de Fatima* (Madrid, 1976), p. 104.

List of Abbreviations

BMK: *Błogosławiony Maksymilian Kolbe, Wybór Pism* (Warsaw, 1973).

KMK: *Konferencje świętego Maksymiliana Marii Kolbego* (Niepokalanów, 1990).

KR: Fr. Anselm W. Romb, OFM Conv., ed., *The Kolbe Reader* (Libertyville: Franciscan Marytown Press, 1987).

LGM: Saint Louis Marie de Montfort, *Traité de la vraie dévotion à la Sainte Vierge, Oeuvres complètes de saint Louis Marie Grignion de Montfort* (Paris, 1966).

SLF: *Schwester Lucia spricht über Fatima*, 5. ed. (Fatima, 1987).

GWPR: Graber, *Die marianischen Weltrundschreiben der Päpste in den letzten hundert Jahren* (Würzburg, 1951).

FSM: C. Feckes, *Die Heilsgeschichtliche Stellvertretung der Menschheit durch Maria* (Paderborn, 1954).

PL: Migne, J. P., *Patrologiae cursus completus. Series latina* (Paris, 1857).

Part One

The Fundamental Law of Action and Reaction

The Fundamental Law of Action and Reaction

God is an eternal, infinite ocean, the fullness of Being. God creates out of love; he brings creatures into being out of nothing and grants that they themselves may be and have existence. The highest creatures are endowed with understanding and will and thus are similar to God in their spiritual nature. God's entire work consists of the pouring forth of his light. He is *actus purus*, pure act, the perfect giving and bestowing of what he is. This self-giving of God is his work of creation. All created being proceeds from God (*exitus*). God, too, goes out from himself (*exitus*) and designs the most varied forms and nuances, to which he unceasingly grants being and also the capability of existing. Yet the creatures cannot exist for a moment by themselves; they continually receive their existence from him. Thus this perpetual bestowal of being, which is the act of God's loving self-gift (*exitus*, *fluxus*, *actio*) is the foundation upon which and the atmosphere within which all continues to exist. Nevertheless, creatures live their own being; notwithstanding their absolute dependence upon

God, they are genuinely autonomous entities. Their distinctiveness is not meant to distance them from each other, but is necessary precisely so that they can be united with one another. Only when there are two "thou's" facing each other can they be united. And that is the meaning of creation: The only reason that God has for "setting it outside himself" is so that he can then unite himself with the infinitely inferior creature that he created out of nothing, draw it back to himself, or let it to return to him (*reditus*). Having its source in God's love and having been created out of nothing, it now flows back to God in love (*refluxus*). Thus it responds to God's loving *actio* by a grateful *re-actio*, and this return to God is its sole meaning and its only goal. Sin, in contrast, consists of deliberately failing to accomplish this *re-actio*. A sinful creature, of course, continually receives the full wealth of the divine creative act, but then it egotistically wills to keep this wealth for itself and refuses to acknowledge that it is completely and utterly dependent upon God, that it will only be happy if it fulfills his will, that is, if it returns to God's perfect fullness and receives there the fulfillment of all its longings and hopes.

Saint Maximilian puts it this way:

> Everywhere in the universe we encounter action and a reaction equal but contrary to that action: coming and going, departure and return, division and reunification. Division, however, is always in view of reunification, for the latter is creative. This is nothing but a reflection of the most Holy Trinity in the activity of creatures. Unification is love, creative love. God's activity outside of himself does not proceed differently: God creates the universe, and this is in some way a separation. But by means of the natural law given to them by God, creatures perfect

> themselves, become like unto God, return to him. Reasonable creatures, in addition, love him consciously and unite themselves to him even more by means of that love; they return towards him. In addition, the creature entirely filled with this love, with the divinity, is the Immaculata, the one without even the slightest stain of sin, the one who never deviated in any way from the will of God.[6]

This formulation of the meaning of all created things is essentially no different from that found in Saint Augustine's famous statement: "Thou hast made us for Thyself, O Lord, and our hearts are restless until they rest in Thee!"

We notice this again and again in our everyday life:

> Man would like to be great, wise, rich, famous, happy, loving, and loved. Yet no happiness on earth can fulfill him. He longs for more, always for something more. When will this longing finally be fulfilled? Even if he experienced the greatest happiness, as soon as he notices a limit to it, his thirst surpasses it and he says, 'Oh, if only this limit, too, would someday give way to infinity!' What happiness is he yearning for, then? For a happiness without limits, without any limit whatsoever either in intensity or in magnitude, in its continuance or in anything. The only happiness of this sort is God, the infinite source of all happiness. Therefore the soul yearns to possess God himself. But how does it want to possess him, to be united with this happiness? As perfectly as possible! To become one with him without limitation. Here, too, is corroborated the splendid law of action and reaction, which the Creator has imprinted upon every created activity as the hallmark of the life

6. Final article of February 17, 1941, BMK, pp. 597-598; English translation in: Fr. Anselm W. Romb, OFM Conv., ed., *The Kolbe Reader* (Libertyville: Franciscan Marytown Press, 1987) [henceforth KR], p. 211.

> of the most Holy Trinity. Creation has come forth from the hand of the Almighty and now is returning to him. It doesn't rest, until it becomes 'God himself' (by grace).[7]

Furthermore this flowing back to God and into God is the movement of the love of all the blessed in heaven through all eternity. The infinite happiness of the eternal "fulfillment with the whole fullness of God" is an "eternal rest" that contains an infinitely effervescent life and movement. It is the fulfillment of the deepest yearning of our hearts, which Blessed Elizabeth of the Trinity expresses so profoundly: "O my Three, my All, my Blessedness, eternally One, Immensity in which I lose myself, I deliver myself to you as your prey. Descend entirely into me, so that I may be immersed in you, waiting until I shall advance so far as to behold the abyss of your glory in your light."[8]

But what good is all that to me, since I cannot reach heaven by my own power?

> My God, my only happiness, how can I come to know you even better? I see your creatures and thank you and love you, but they are not enough for me, as you know very well, for I do not see you, I do not hear you. I would like to become like you, according to your will, but how? You are purest spirit, I am flesh. Tell me what I should do; show me my destination. Show me how I, a fleshly human being, can be perfected, can become like you, purest spirit, can become divinized! And God descends to earth and becomes man: the God-man. Jesus Christ himself leads by his example and teaches by his word. Souls that love God came in throngs to make themselves copies of this original image, to conform themselves to him, to unite themselves to him, to be trans-

7. Fragment of his unfinished book, BMK p. 614.

8. Elisabeth de la Trinité, *Oeuvres complètes* (Paris, 1991), p. 200.

> formed into him. In order to draw the soul to himself in love and to transform it into himself, Christ showed his boundless love, his heart ardent with love for souls. This heart required him to allow himself to be nailed to the cross, to remain with us in the Eucharist and to enter into our souls, and finally, as his last will and testament, to give us his own mother to be our mother.[9]

Thus we see God's whole work as a great movement of love, which pours forth from God and flows back to him again. This perpetual stream is the meaning and purpose of all creation; it is the essence of heaven. But how, concretely, did God establish this movement of love? His *actio* consists first of all in the creation of the world. After original sin and man's fall from grace, the Father sends the Son to redeem mankind. Finally, the Father and the Son send the Holy Ghost to sanctify men and bring them to perfection. Now what is the first dwelling place, the first abode that the triune God finds when he condescends to be with his creatures? In other words, who is the endpoint, the *terminus* of God's *actio* in the world? The Immaculata!

> [T]he creature entirely filled with this love [of God], is the Immaculate, the one without even the slightest stain of sin, the one who never deviated in any way from the will of God. She is joined in an ineffable manner to the Holy Ghost because she is his spouse; but this is true of her in an incomparably more perfect sense than anything this term can express among creatures. What kind of union is this? It is above all interior; it is the union of her very being with the being of the Holy Ghost. The Holy Ghost dwells in her, lives in her, from the first instant of her existence, and he will do so always, throughout eternity.[10]

9. Ibid., p. 615.

10. Final article, KR, p. 211.

But it is not enough to say this. Mary is not only the last rung of the ladder that leads down from God to creation, but also the beginning of the return to God, in which all the divine life that has been bestowed upon creation goes back again to God. And just as the divine life descended from the Father through the Son in the Holy Ghost into the heart of the Immaculata, and from there continues to flow into all other creatures, so too this life returns from all creatures through Mary in the Holy Ghost to the Son and from the Son back to the Father. She stands on the highest rung of the created ladder and personally receives God, who comes down to earth. She is the summit of creation and the bridge over which all paths from heaven and to heaven travel, the nave of the church that bridges the distance between God's majesty and the guilty sinner and connects these two extremes.

Before we enter into this mystery of the Immaculata, we would like to illustrate the reality just described with a well-known vision, the revelation of God to Sister Lucy in Tuy on June 13, 1929. On July 13, 1917, the mother of God had announced at Fatima that she would come again "to request the consecration of Russia to my Immaculate Heart and the communion of reparation on the First Saturday of the month." In fact, the mother of God appeared with the Christ Child to Lucia in December of 1925, when she was a postulant in Pontevedra, to explain to her the nature of the devotion to her Immaculate Heart. And on June 13, 1929, between 11:00 and 12:00 at night, the apparition in Tuy took place, in which Mary called for the consecration of Russia to her Immaculate Heart. Sister Lucia describes this vision as follows:

> Suddenly the whole chapel became bright with a supernatural light, and above the altar appeared a luminous cross that extended to the ceiling. In an

even brighter light appeared above the cross the face of a man with his body down to the waist. In front of his chest was a dove, also made entirely of light, and nailed to the cross was the body of another man. A little below his hips appeared a chalice floating in the air and a large host, upon which fell the drops of blood that streamed from the face of the Crucified and from his wounded side. They flowed down upon the host, and from there they fell into the chalice.

> Beneath the cross to the right was our Lady with her Immaculate Heart in her hand (it was our Lady of Fatima with her Immaculate Heart, which she held in her left hand, without a sword or roses, but rather surrounded with a crown of thorns and all aflame).
>
> Beneath the cross on the left appeared large letters, as though made of crystal-clear water, that flowed from the hand of the Crucified down upon the altar and formed the following words: Grace and Mercy.
>
> I understood that the mystery of the most Holy Trinity was being shown to me; and I received insights into this mystery that I am not allowed to reveal.[11]

Sister Lucy goes on to record the words that the mother of God spoke during this vision, namely the request that the Holy Father, together with all the bishops of the world, should consecrate Russia to her Immaculate Heart, and that in this way Russia will be saved.

Certainly the first purpose of this apparition is the consecration of Russia and thus the fulfillment of God's great promises through Mary at Fatima. But why did Mary want to combine this revelation with the vision of the most Holy Trinity? Surely in order to show that the ultimate purpose and deepest meaning of her apparitions is founded upon this mystery: that all

11. SLF, p. 209.

the particular graces that she wants to give the world through Fatima (and other apparitions) are intended to direct people to a very profound reality, namely the true meaning of the Immaculata in the mystery of God and Redemption.

Everything comes from God the Father, who sends the Son to the world and together with the Son spirates [breathes out] the Holy Ghost. The Father is the primordial source of all being, of all life, of all love. From the bosom of the Father, the Son is begotten and the Holy Ghost is spirated.

The mission of the Son is the redemption of the world upon the cross. In the vision at Tuy the cross takes up the whole room, from the altar to the ceiling. The cross is the revelation of God's love in its entirety; through the Crucified all "grace and mercy" is granted to us. The blood that flows from the Redeemer's wounds is collected in the mystery of the host and the chalice: Christ's entire work of redemption is present in the most Holy Eucharist, in which the Sacrifice on Calvary is re-presented and renewed.

The mission of the Holy Ghost is the "illumination" of the whole work of redemption, namely making all of God's love shine forth as light, grace and strength, and thus bringing God's entire work to perfection.

This action, God's self-giving, his descent into the world for us and for our salvation, is collected in the heart of the Immaculata, which is entirely luminous from the light of the Holy Ghost and which receives into itself all of God's love. Her heart is the palpable expression of her inmost being: of her soul, which is completely filled with the Holy Ghost; of her intelligence, which is full of unfathomable wisdom; of her will, which is full of devotion and love. She alone stands there beneath the cross as the new Eve beside the new Adam, so as to bring forth with him the redeemed human race. She stands there as the first fruit of the redemptive sacrifice, to which she owes the miracle of her Immaculate Conception. Her heart appears pierced by the thorns of Christ's crown of thorns: it means that she is the co-Redemptrix, who of all creatures shares most fully in his suffering. She holds this heart in her hand, that is, she holds it out to us, she gives it to us, for she is our mother. Enkindled by the Spirit of Love, her heart burns for her children, whom she bore on Mount Calvary amidst a thousand pains, and which she now desires to snatch at all costs from eternal destruction.

The Immaculata with her radiant heart now touches our world. From her flows this entire love-filled outpouring of the Trinity further into souls. This is God's *actio*, the initial movement of divine love, which the doctors of the Church call the "going forth" or the *exitus*. This *actio* is also symbolized by the flowing, living water that pours out of the wound of the Crucified down into the world as "grace and mercy".

But the second movement is clearly indicated in this vision, too: the return (*reditus*), the response (*re-actio*), the flowing-back (*refluxus*) of creation to God. By the same path which God took to descend to us, we are supposed to return to him. *My Immaculate Heart will be your refuge and the way that leads you to God!* Mary's message during this revelation can be summed up in three words, which are also the principal themes of the Fatima message: *consecratio, reparatio, conversio*—consecration, reparation, conversion. Mary comes to the aid of Christianity in its tribulations, draws men to her Immaculate Heart (consecration), leads them back to God (conversion) and calls them to participate in the building up of Christ's kingly reign (reparation).

"The time has come...," Mary began her message in Tuy. At Fatima, the will of God was made visible to the whole world, so that now, in the end times, Mary might be made known to the world as the Mediatrix of All Graces, as the beginning of creation's return home to God. Mary's heart gathers the children of God and preserves in them the light of grace in the midst of a dark world. In her heart we can endure to the end beneath the cross of Christ. And thus proceeds the return through Mary to Christ in the Holy Ghost to the Father.

The Vision at Tuy

Part Two

God's Work in the World Through the Immaculata

(Actio Dei in Mundo per Immaculatam)

Chapter One

God's Work of Creation Through the Immaculata

In the beginning God created heaven and earth and all things visible and invisible. How did he create the world? This will always remain his secret, hidden within the depths of the Trinity for all eternity. Creation out of nothing is something proper to God alone, and no creature can comprehend it. The creature can only determine the beginning and the endpoint of the act of creation, the *terminus a quo* and the *terminus ad quem*. At the starting point (*terminus a quo*) God alone is there, an infinite ocean of being and besides him nothing. At the endpoint, the *terminus ad quem*, creation is there in its paradisiacal beauty. The creation of the world allows our understanding to have a glimpse into God himself, according to the analogy with an earthly "maker", "artist", or "architect". From his work the master builder is known. This manifests the infinite wisdom and intelligence of God, which devises all natures, as well as his all-surpassing power of bestowing existence upon this enormous variety. From the design of the work, its order and harmony, and also from the behavior of the creatures, one can draw conclusions evocative as to the way in which God created the world. One can say that God had an order and a hierarchy of beings in mind, that all things are guided by the law that God gave them. One can also determine that God acts according to his own nature and that therefore every created thing is a trace, an image and likeness of God.

These findings, however, as important as they are, give us only a pale insight into how great and unfathomable a mystery the act of creation really is. Only God himself can reveal to us what his work is at its deepest foundation and how he accomplished this work.

People often pose the question as to the temporal unfolding of the work of creation. There is the theory of the evolution of things starting from the "Big Bang" and continuing through the higher development of the species, leading up to man. About this theory we should note first that every advance from a lower to a higher species must be accompanied by God and his creative power, for the lower form does not have the capability of bringing about something higher by itself, according to the fundamental law: *agere sequitur esse*—action follows being and corresponds to it. One cannot give what one does not possess. Furthermore it should be noted that this theory regards the act of creation from the viewpoint of man, who is bound by the dimensions of space and time. God, however, stands unlimited beyond space and time, and these dimensions first came into being when he created the world. Therefore the act of creation itself lies outside of them and beyond them. Thus Sacred Scripture can say that God created "all things at once," *omnia simul* (*Eccl.* 18:1), and presents the work of creation as a sequence of six days (*Gen.* 1). The mystery remains.

Eternal Wisdom – Created Wisdom

Yet we can say something more about this work: God, who is eternal, has all of creation with its marvelous order eternally in mind, even though it has a beginning in time. And so for all eternity God sees the whole world before him, as he has designed it, in brilliant purity and perfection. The divine architect has, as it were, a blueprint before him, which he designed in eternity. *The Book of Proverbs* speaks of this original plan:

> The Lord possessed me in the beginning of his ways, before he made any thing from the beginning. I was set up from eternity, and of old before the earth was made. The depths were not as yet, and I was already conceived, neither had the fountains of waters as yet sprung out: The mountains with their huge bulk had not as yet been established: before the hills I was brought forth: He had not yet made the earth, nor the rivers, nor the poles of the world. When he prepared the heavens, I was present: when with a certain law and compass he enclosed the depths: When he established the sky above, and poised the fountains of waters, when he compassed the sea with its bounds, and set a law to the waters that they should not pass their limits, when he balanced the foundations of the earth; I was with him forming [ordering] all things (*Prov.* 8:22-30).

The Church in her liturgy applies this passage to the Immaculata. Why? Because the creation of the world has as its goal the Incarnation of the Son of God and thereby the union of creation with God. In God, the cause and purpose of creation are one and the same. This first principle and the final goal, however, is Christ, the Redeemer. And because God ordained from all eternity that Christ should desire to come to earth through his mother, Mary becomes the maternal cause of all things.

> She is the mother of all things and God the Father is the origin of all things: everything that is, *per se*, the source and cause of a cause is also, *per se*, the source and cause of everything caused. But she herself is the mother of him who is the cause and source of all. Therefore she is, *per se*, the mother of all things.[12]

The Second person of the most Blessed Trinity, the

12. St. Albert the Great, *Mariale,* quaestio 141, in: C. De Koninck, *Ego Sapientia, La Sagesse qui est Marie* (Laval, 1943), p. 158.

eternal Word, is the exemplary cause (*causa exemplaris*) of all created being and as such the eternal, uncreated Wisdom: "All things were made by him, and without him was made nothing that was made" (*Jn.* 1:3). "[He] is the image of the invisible God, the firstborn of every creature; for in him were all things created in heaven and on earth.... All things were created by him and in him" (*Col.* 1:14-16). In God's eternal plan, Christ, as the son of Mary, is the firstborn of all creation and, again in his capacity as Mary's son, is the head and crowning glory of the universe.

> "It follows that Mary, too, was predestined with Christ, and if Christ assumes the first place in this predestination, then Mary receives the second. Christ is the sun, and Mary—the moon, which shines more brightly than all the other stars together. What is Woman, that Thou art mindful of her, that Thou visitest her?! Thou hast crowned her with glory and honor and hast set her over the work of Thy hands. Thou hast subjected all things under her feet [paraphrase of *Ps.* 8:5-8]; Thou hast not made her a little less than the angels [*cf.* Ps 8:6] but hast exalted her above all the choirs of angels. Thou hast clothed her with the sun and given her the brightest stars as a crown. [...] This divine predestination is, so to speak, the prefigurement and prototype of the universal Church of God's elect. When God presented to Moses the likeness of the divine dwelling place, he spoke first about the Ark of the Covenant; similarly, in his original plan for his creation, God thought first of the Blessed Virgin as the living ark of his Godhead.[13]

The perfect copy, the most complete, pure, and immaculate "imitation" of the eternal Word is the Immaculata. The Son, the eternal Wisdom, is God.

13. St. Lawrence of Brindisi, *Opera omnia*, Pars I (Padua, 1928), cited in: C. Feckes, *Die Heilsgeschichtliche Stellvertretung der Menschheit durch Maria* (Paderborn, 1954) [henceforth HSM], p. 211.

The Immaculata, the perfect copy of the eternal Wisdom is the first and perfect creature, which includes all the properties of the eternal Wisdom. That is why the Church calls her "the created wisdom" and applies to her the properties of the eternal Wisdom.

"I was with Him forming all things" (Prov. 8:30)

Forming and ordering is a property of wisdom. God wills his creation to be orderly, and this order is the cause of harmony and beauty. Its order is supposed to reproduce the interior order of God. The order is, so to speak, a plan which harmoniously assembles the various elements into a marvelous structure. Building a cathedral requires an extraordinary intelligence, which thinks through the plan of this highly complex construction project and assembles the component parts according to the laws of physics and architecture. Often such ingenious plans are never carried out completely. If one compares them with what has actually been built, these plans are often much more beautiful and magnificent. By analogy one can say that God still has a plan for all of creation, an original plan, an original concept (*conceptio*), in which all things have their intended purpose and are designed to be in perfect harmony. This all-encompassing, ordering plan is entirely without stain: "For she is a vapor of the power of God, and a certain pure emanation of the glory of the Almighty God, and therefore no defiled thing cometh into her" (*Wis*. 7:25): *Immaculata conceptio*.

Thus Mary stands at the origin of the entire universe: "*Ego sum radix*"—I am the root.[14] This original plan "reacheth therefore from end to end mightily and ordereth all things sweetly" (*Wis*. 8:1). All creatures taken together do not attain to the surpassing beauty of this original creature, this divine masterpiece: "For she is

14. Tract of the Mass in honor of the B.V.M., Mediatrix of All Graces.

more beautiful than the sun, and above all the order of the stars; being compared with the light, she is found before it. For after this cometh night, but no evil can overcome wisdom" (*Wis.* 7:29-30). After her pattern and example God grants being to every creature, and the perfection of each one of them consists of its participation in the immaculate, universal prototype, and only in union with her does a creature arrive at its exalted destination: "And being but one, she can do all things: and remaining in herself the same, she reneweth all things, and through nations conveyeth herself into holy souls, she maketh the friends of God and prophets. For God loveth none but him that dwelleth with wisdom" (*Wis.* 7:27-28). This is what the doctors of the Church mean when they see in the Immaculata the exemplary cause of all creation. Herein is the theological reason why the Church Fathers so lavishly attribute to Mary the characteristics of all the most beautiful creatures in order to illustrate her greatness and beauty. Thus not only is the rose a reflection of her beauty, the lily a symbol of her purity, the mountain a symbol of her power, the stars a symbol of her radiance, etc., but she herself is the prototype according to which all the beauties of creation have been formed. Every flower has its beauty from her and reproduces the flower of Mary's soul. The fragrance of the lily is a further emanation of the lovely fragrance of Mary's soul; the majesty of the lofty mountain is an imitation of the majesty of her being; the human soul is a more or less faint copy of her soul. The German poet Novalis is speaking along these lines when he meditates on the mystery of woman: "O Mary, I see thee expressed in a thousand images." And Saint Bernardine of Siena professes:

> From the final perfection that has been granted to her alone, the Blessed Virgin imparts to all the

> natures and perfections of the world their ultimate essential value, richness, and exalted status. All being was directed toward one foremost being: the living being toward the most noble life, the sentient being toward the most exquisite sensibility; all womanly conception toward one most precious fruit of the womb; all births toward the best nature that can be born; all things endowed with reason toward a unique rational being; all things endowed with spirit toward a most excellent spiritual being; in short, all creatures seek to become united with a being that is best in its pure created nature. That being the case, provisions were made for the world by means of a woman who is blessed above all: only once did she become a mother, and through this unique motherhood she brought all sorts of created things to their highest and ultimate perfection.[15]

For You God Created the World....

But there is yet another sense in which Mary participates in the first divine act, God's act of creation. Everyone who does something, does it for some purpose (*omnis agens agit propter finem*). If God, so to speak, comes out of his interior trinitarian life in order to create, then he always has in mind the goal for which he does all this, namely, "the praise of his glory" (*Eph.* 1:6). He, Christ, is the rightful heir of the ages, the Omega, the destination toward which everything is ordered from all eternity.

> For Christ's honor and glory God called the universe into existence ... the world, heaven and earth, and all that is concealed in the heavens. Whatever is in a kingdom is there for the king and must serve him. Christ, however, says, 'All power is given to Me in

15. St. Bernardine of Siena, *Sermo 5 de nativitate BMV*, in: P. Sträter, S.J., *Maria in der Offenbarung* (Paderborn, 1962), p. 275.

> heaven and on earth' (*Mt.* 28:18). [...] As he began to devise plans for his royal castle in this world, God foreordained Christ as the sure, strong, and firm foundation, which forever guarantees the restoration of the building, should it be damaged in the storms of time. And because the Architect of the world founded the construction of the world, with its being, its grace and glory, upon Christ in this way, he can love everything only for Christ's sake. All of creation, the Church and Paradise, nature and the supernatural, is the royal banquet which God the King hosts out of love and respect for his royal Son.[16]

Therefore, if Christ as man, as Mary's son, is the objective for which the world was created, then Mary, too, is the objective, in him and dependent upon him. The great scriptural exegete Cornelius à Lapide comments as follows on two verses from the Book of Ecclesiastes: "I made that in the heavens there should rise light that never faileth" (*Eccl.* 24:6); "I, Wisdom, have poured out rivers" (*Eccl.* 24:40).

> In the literal sense we should read: I was the reason why God created the light, the heavens, the sea, the rivers and the entire universe. For God's creation was ordered to the purpose of justifying and glorifying the saints, a work that Christ accomplished by means of the Blessed Virgin. For the order of nature was created and established for the sake of the order of grace. Now because the Blessed Virgin is the mother of Christ and consequently has become the mediatrix of the entire order of grace established by Christ, for that same reason she became the final cause of the creation of the universe. For the purpose of the universe is Christ, his mother, and the saints. That means that this universe was created so that the saints might enjoy grace and eternal glory through the mediation of Christ and of

16. St. Lawrence of Brindisi, HSM, p. 232 – 233.

> the Blessed Virgin. Although Christ and Mary are parts of the universe and consequently later than the universe with regard to their material cause (*causa materialis*), nevertheless they are prior to the universe according to their final cause. Therefore there is a certain mutual dependence between the creation of the universe and the coming of Christ and of the Blessed Virgin. God willed the birth of Christ and of Mary in no other manner than in this world. And furthermore he did not will the existence of this world without Christ and Mary; indeed, he had created it on their account. He willed that the entire universe and also the order of grace be related and ordered to Christ and the Blessed Virgin as their fulfillment and purpose. Accordingly, Christ and the Blessed Virgin are the final cause of the creation of the universe, and at the same time they are its formal cause, *i.e.*, its prototype, its original plan. For the order of grace, in which Christ and Mary assume first place, is the idea and the prototype according to which God created and arranged the order of nature and the entire universe.[17]

And so with astonishment we realize that even at the beginning of his work *ad extra*, God had the Immaculata with him. She is the first creature, chosen before the foundation of the world, so as to be, in and with Christ, the prototype, the original plan, the exemplar and final cause of all that exists. Overwhelmed by this mystery, Saint Maximilian Kolbe exclaims:

> Allow me to praise you, O most holy Virgin.... In you alone is God worshiped incomparably more than in all his saints. For you God created the world. For you God also called me into existence. Why is such good fortune granted me? O let me praise you, most Blessed Virgin![18]

17. Cornelius à Lapide, *Commentaria in Ecclesiasticum*, ch. 24, vers. 1-2, Edition Crampon, Vives, Vol. 9, p. 618.
18. *Rycerz Niepokalanej* Nr. 18, 1939, BMK, p. 587 – 588.

Chapter Two

The Sending of the Son into the World Through the Immaculata

For what purpose did God create the world? He brings forth created beings and sets them apart from himself, so that they in freedom might be united again with him, might return to him. God is love; out of love he creates out of nothing. Everything that exists is a shining forth of his love. But love wants to be loved in return.

The Angelic World and the Immaculata

So God first created the "invisible" world of the pure spirits. According to the opinion of many Fathers and doctors of the Church, the mystery of the Incarnation was made known to the angels and presented to them for a decision. They were supposed to worship Mary's son as their head and king of creation and acknowledge Mary, the mother, as their mistress.[19] Saint Maximilian Kolbe explains this:

> In creating the angels, God wanted them freely to offer proof that they were willing to fulfill his will always and in everything. He revealed to them the mystery of the Incarnation and foretold that he

19. The patristic passages are cited by St. Lawrence of Brindisi, who also advocates this doctrine. See HSM, p. 223 – 224.

would call into being a human being, consisting of body and soul, and that he would exalt this being to the dignity of the mother of God, and that she would therefore become their queen and must be honored by them as such. Countless hosts of angelic spirits joyously greeted the Woman whom the Creator determined to exalt so highly and humbly gave honor to their mistress. A certain group, however, headed by Lucifer, forgot that all that they were and possessed they had received from God, and that otherwise, of themselves, they were absolutely nothing. And so they became indignant and were unwilling to submit to God's will. Indeed, they thought that they were something much higher than a human being endowed with a body. Honoring something like that seemed to be beneath their dignity, and so they proudly rose up and refused to do the will of God. In return they immediately received their punishment, eternal punishment: being cast from the presence of God, hell. Because pure spirits possess keen understanding and their deed was therefore quite deliberate and done with full consent, their sin had the qualities of a mortal sin committed with full awareness. And so those angels became devils for all eternity. The very Woman who became for the good angels a confirmation in grace and an assurance of eternal happiness became instead, for the devils, a stumbling block and the cause of their rejection, and since then the memory of this fact fills them with an infernal hatred against her, similar to the hatred that they have for God, whose faithful image she is.[20]

Thus the Immaculata accompanies God's work in the invisible world of spirits, too. In keeping with God's will, their eternal happiness or unhappiness is connected with her personally.

20. Fragment of his unfinished book on the Immaculata, August 1940, BMK, p. 593.

The Promise of the Savior's Coming in the Immaculata

Man, too, refused to love God when he was tempted by the devil and allowed himself to be deceived by him. Since man, however, does not possess the all-encompassing intelligence of the pure spirits, and furthermore did not sin on his own initiative but rather fell out of weakness, God decreed in his eternal providence not to allow the work of his hands to suffer eternal ruin. He who had "established" the universe "in wondrous dignity", resolved to restore it "even more admirably".[21] In this second work of God in the world, his interior nature as infinite love is manifested much more magnificently than in his first deed, the act of creation. The sin of our first parents had punishments as its necessary consequence, but at the moment when they were driven out of paradise and lost immortality and their friendship with God, God promised mankind a future redemption, specifically, that the day would come when Satan's bonds would be loosed. "I will put enmities between thee and the Woman, and thy seed and her seed: she shall crush thy head and thou shalt lie in wait for her heel" (*Gen.* 3:15). If mankind had not obtained this light, they would have despaired. So instead this first glad tiding was given to them at the very beginning (and that is why this promise is called the *Protoevangelium*), and this first hope is the Woman and her offspring, Mary and her divine son.[22] The Church's magisterial teaching confirms this:

> These ecclesiastical writers [the fathers and doctors of the Church] in quoting the words by which at the

21. Offertory of the Holy Mass.

22. For proof that the Protoevangelium refers to Mary and for its theological significance, see H.L. Barth, *Ipsa Conteret, Maria die Schlangenzertreterin* (Ruppichteroth, 2000), especially pp. 83-94.

> beginning of the world God announced his merciful remedies prepared for the regeneration of mankind—words by which he crushed the audacity of the deceitful serpent and wondrously raised up the hope of our race, saying, 'I will put enmities between you and the Woman, between your seed and her seed'—taught that by this divine prophecy the merciful Redeemer of mankind, Jesus Christ, the only-begotten Son of God, was clearly foretold: That his most Blessed Mother, the Virgin Mary, was prophetically indicated; and, at the same time, the very enmity of both against the evil one was significantly expressed. Hence, just as Christ, the mediator between God and man, assumed human nature, blotted the handwriting of the decree that stood against us, and fastened it triumphantly to the cross, so too the most holy Virgin, united with him by a most intimate and indissoluble bond, was, with him and through him, eternally at enmity with the evil serpent, and most completely triumphed over him, and thus crushed his head with her immaculate foot.[23]

Of all the prophets, Isaiah describes most clearly the Savior who is to come, and he promises that he will be the son born of a virgin (*Isa.* 7:14). The wisdom literature of the Old Testament praises the Woman who is to come as God's "beloved" (*Cant.* 2:16) and as "the king's daughter" (*Ps.* 44:14). The Woman who will crush the serpent "cometh forth as the morning rising, fair as the moon, bright as the sun, terrible as an army set in array" (*Cant.* 6:9). "Thou art all fair, O my love, and there is not a spot in thee" (*Cant.* 4:7). Thus, from the very beginning, the Immaculata is at the focal point of the promises. Actually God could have redeemed the world in any one of many possible ways. What matters for us is the reality, namely the way that he in fact chose.

23. Pius IX., Bull *Ineffabilis Deus*, [Eng. ref.].

"God has decided to begin and accomplish his greatest works through the Blessed Virgin ever since he created her, [and] we can safely believe that he will not change his plan in the time to come, for he is God and does not change in his thoughts or his way of acting."[24]

The Incarnation in the Immaculata

The popes, the fathers, and doctors of the Church, theologians and saints never tire of praising this coming of God's Son to us through Mary. Saint Louis Marie de Montfort writes that God made himself, as it were, dependent upon her.

> God-made-man found freedom in imprisoning himself in her womb. He displayed power in allowing himself to be borne by this young maiden. He found his glory and that of his Father in hiding his splendors from all creatures here below and revealing them only to Mary. He glorified his independence and his majesty in depending upon this lovable virgin in his conception, his birth, his presentation in the temple, and in the thirty years of his hidden life [and] even at his death.[25]

And Saint Maximilian Kolbe summarizes this mystery in a very profound expression: *Gesta Dei per Immaculatam*—God's exploits, God's mighty deeds through the Immaculata. "Something incomprehensible happens: God lowers himself to the level of his creature, becomes man, in order to save us and to teach us humility, recollection, obedience, and truth."[26] But he does not wish to come to earth, like the first Adam, as a grown man, but rather he wills to be "like us in all things but sin" and to be born as a child from the womb of a mother.

24. St. Louis Marie de Montfort, *True Devotion,* par. 15, p. 6.
25. *Ibid.*, p. [little further on].
26. *Rycerz Niepokalanej,* Nr. 5, 1926, p. 2.

> Among the countless multitude of possible beings which reproduce his various perfections, God also saw from all eternity the being which is perfect in every respect and marred by no stain of sin, which imitates his divine attributes as faithfully as a finite creature ever could. He rejoiced at the sight and decided from all eternity to call her into being at a predetermined time.[27]

And this hour then came, in which she was to fulfill her eminent mission alongside her son. Are not all creatures created for the Son? Therefore if the Son wishes to come into his creation, in order to bring it back home to God, then it is also time to call into concrete existence that Woman whom he had always had in mind as the immaculate prototype, the masterwork of his hands, the creature in whom he is well pleased for all eternity, because she alone is completely faithful to him and reflects him with utter purity.

Precisely on account of her purity he creates her at that precise moment, since she alone is worthy to become the dwelling place and sanctuary into which the All-Holy One descends. She is like a high mountain in the midst of all creation; while the latter looks like a dirty heap of gravel, the high mountain is utterly pure, quite spotless, completely devoted to God. God comes down to the peak of this mountain and descends "from the everlasting hills" into our valley of tears.

> In her there took place the union between God and creation. The Father, as though he were her spouse, entrusted his Son to her; the Son descended into her virginal womb and became her son; while the Holy Ghost formed in her womb in a most marvellous manner the body of Jesus, the humanity of Jesus.[28]

27. Fragment of his unfinished book on the Immaculata, August 1940, BMK, p. 593.
28. KR, p. 191 [modified].

And so Mary becomes the necessary instrument of his Incarnation. Indeed, he makes his coming into the world and thus the homecoming of creation back to him, our salvation, and our eternal happiness dependent upon her from the first moment. For Mary is not a passive, indifferent instrument of God; rather, she is free and deliberate in her decision, which God himself waits for. This answer by Mary, in its momentous greatness, is profoundly related to the creative Word of God himself: "In the beginning, God said, 'Let there be . . .' and creation came to be. And now the creature Mary says, 'Fiat—Let it be done to me,' and God came to be ... in her."[29]

Mary responds to this *actio* of God in the most perfect manner: her *fiat* is so great, so total, so thoroughly in keeping with the truth, so humble, and her love is so immeasurably strong and pure and unhesitating, that God is, so to speak, attracted by her and comes to her, so intimately that he himself becomes man in her, takes on flesh from her flesh, blood from her blood, his heart from her heart. And now Mary is no longer just the purest of all creatures, the realization of God's original concept, his masterpiece, "not only God's child but, what is more, God's mother, and not only his adoptive mother, but really and truly the mother of God. And that is not just a hypothesis, a probability, but something sure, complete certainty, a dogma of the Faith.

But are you still today the mother of God? The title of motherhood never changes. In eternity God will say to you, 'My mother'. The lawgiver who established the fourth commandment will honor you in eternity, for ever.[30] We can never meditate enough on this, the greatest mystery of Mary: "We know what 'mother' means.

29. [in:] J. Domański, *Zarys myśli maryjnej św. Maksymiliana Marii Kolbego* (Niepokalanów, 1993), p. 31.
30. *Rycerz Niepokalanej,* Nr. 18, 1939, p. 129-130.

But with our limited understanding we cannot grasp what 'mother of God' means; only God himself can know that completely."[31]

The significance of Mary is so great that she is drawn into the interior life of the most Holy Trinity.[32] Because she possesses with the heavenly Father the same Son, Mary becomes through her motherhood a "blood relative of the Trinity" (*consanguinea trinitatis*), as the Church fathers say. Christ himself confirms this, when he on the one hand speaks of his Father in heaven and on the other hand calls himself the son of man, *i.e.,* son of Mary. And the Holy Ghost uses her as his instrument by forming Christ's human nature in her and through her. In this sense Saint Hesychius of Jerusalem calls Mary "the *pleroma* of the most Holy Trinity",[33] the completion or complement of the Trinity:

> what he means by that are the emanations of trinitarian life into the world of creatures, the continuations and imitations of this infinite life, as they are realized in creative life. Viewed in this way, God's Son gains through Mary's motherhood a new sonship, which is the mirror image of his eternal sonship. He receives the new titles: Redeemer, Lord, the Firstborn among many brethren. The Father and the Holy Ghost enter into new relations with the God-man, which did not exist in the absence of Mary's motherhood.[34]

But if God made the sending of the eternal Word into the world dependent in advance upon the Immaculata and thus "began the salvation of the world through Mary", and if God is always the same and his way of proceeding is always the same, then the law for-

31. O. Domański, *op. cit.* p. 32.
32. See Part Four.
33. *De sancta Deipara Maria Homilia, Sermo 5,* MG, 93, p. 1461.
34. C. Feckes, *Die Gottesmutterschaft,* [in:] P. Sträter, *Maria in der Glaubenswissenschaft* (Paderborn, 1962), pp. 66-67.

mulated by Saint Bernard is in fact true: "It is God's will that we have everything through Mary." Her motherhood unites her so closely with the mission of her son, that the earliest fathers of the Church already saw in her the new Eve, who together with and in dependence upon the new Adam redeems the world. Her 'Yes' to God is the beginning of her mission as co-Redemptrix. Leo XIII corroborates this:

> The eternal Son of God, about to take upon him our nature for the saving and ennobling of man, and about to consummate thus a mystical union between himself and all mankind, did not accomplish his design without adding there the free consent of the elect mother, who represented in some sort all human kind, according to the illustrious and just opinion of Saint Thomas, who says that the Annunciation was effected with the consent of the Virgin standing in the place of humanity. With equal truth may it be also affirmed that, by the will of God, Mary is the intermediary through whom is distributed unto us this immense treasure of mercies gathered by God, for mercy and truth were created by Jesus Christ (*Jn.* 1:17). Thus as no man goeth to the Father but by the Son, so no man goeth to Christ but by his mother.[35]

Thus, from the moment of her *fiat*, Mary is the *socia redemptoris*—the associate of the Redeemer who accompanies Christ throughout the work of redemption, from the crib to the cross.[36]

35. Encyclical *Octobri Mensae*, GWP, p. 48 [English ref.?].

36. In his Encyclical *Miserentissimus Redemptor* (Acta Apostolicae Sedis XX [1928], p. 178), Pius XI says that the, "Virgin mother of God ... brought forth for us Jesus our Redeemer, and nourished him, and offered him as a victim by the cross, by her mystic union with Christ and his very special grace she likewise became and is piously called a reparatress [Reparatrix]." [TRANSLATOR'S NOTE: The expression *socia redemptoris* does not mean "associate in redemption" but rather "the Redeemer's associate"; furthermore, Dr. Miravalle does not catalogue it as appearing in this Encyclical by Pius XI. It may be an expression from an encyclical by some other pope. I have rewritten footnote 36 to include actual language by Pius XI.]

Chapter Three

Christ's Work of Redemption with the Immaculata

The Hidden Life and the Public Life

"I have given you an example, that as I have done to you, so you do also" (*Jn.* 13:15). What example, though, has Jesus given us?

> He begins his mission and his teaching about the way to heaven by making himself dependent upon the Immaculata, as a child depends upon its mother, and by keeping perfectly the fourth commandment. He honors his mother during the thirty-three years of his sojourn on earth and serves her directly in everything, so as to do the will of God the Father. And from that moment on, no one can become like Christ unless he follows his example and honors the Immaculata and devotes himself unreservedly to her.[37]

Saint Louis Marie de Montfort points out that the public life of Jesus, too, is entirely enfolded in the mystery of Mary.

> If we examine closely the remainder of the life of Jesus Christ, we see that he chose to begin his miracles through Mary. It was by her word that he sanctified Saint John the Baptist in the womb of his mother Saint Elizabeth; no sooner had Mary spoken than John was sanctified. This was his first and greatest

37. Saint Maximilian Kolbe, in: J. Domański *op.cit.*, p. 34.

> miracle of grace. At the wedding in Cana he changed water into wine at her humble prayer, and this was his first miracle in the order of nature. He began and continued his miracles through Mary and he will continue them through her until the end of time.[38]

On this subject Pope Leo XIII writes:

> Then Saint John the Baptist, by a singular privilege, is sanctified in his mother's womb and favored with special graces that he might prepare the way of the Lord; and this comes to pass by the greeting of Mary who had been inspired to visit her cousin. At last the expected of nations comes to light, Christ the Savior. The Virgin bears him. And when the shepherds and the wise men, first-fruits of the Christian Faith, come with longing to his cradle, they find there the young Child, with Mary, his mother. Then, that he might before men offer himself as a victim to his heavenly Father, he desires to be taken to the temple; and by the hands of Mary he is there presented to the Lord.[39]

In a veiled way he speaks constantly of her when he calls himself the "Son of man", for he is, after all, the son of only one human being: Mary.

> This discreet presence of Mary in the life of Christ shows us what mankind owes Mary with regard to God's act of becoming man. The Incarnation of the eternal Son of God was accomplished not merely in this unprecedented miracle that took place in Mary's womb, but also and especially in the fact that at least one human being — Mary—was aware of it from the beginning, and deliberately and purposefully cooperated in it, first by her consent, but then also by her generous gift of this mystery to mankind and the world, and finally by her unceasing efforts to present

38. St. Louis Marie de Montfort, *True Devotion*, par. 19, p. 8.
39. Encyclical *Jucunda Semper*, GWP, p. 83.

> this infinitely holy mystery in such forms that will be most easily understandable and acceptable to the people of all times and places.[40]

Christ's Passion and Mary's Compassion

Most importantly, however, Mary appears at the moment when he accomplishes his mission, when his hour has come to redeem the world. Through his suffering and death on the cross he became the Redeemer of the world and the one mediator between God and men. But even here Christ does not want to redeem the world alone. "Mary appears and accompanies Jesus to the place of his suffering, is with him at the moment of his death and receives his lifeless body in her arms when it is taken down from the cross."[41] Beneath the cross she appears as the new Eve, who together with the new Adam brings forth the redeemed human race. Here she is appointed by him to be the mother of mankind; here she suffers with him more than all other human beings together could ever suffer. Here her heart is pierced. Here is accomplished Mary's mission as co-Redemptrix. Pius XII summarizes this participation in the work of redemption as follows:

> It was she, the second Eve, who, free from all sin, original or personal, and always most intimately united with her son, offered him on Golgotha to the eternal Father for all the children of Adam, sin-stained by his unhappy fall, and her mother's rights and mother's love were included in the holocaust. Thus she who, according to the flesh, was the mother of our head, through the added title of pain and glory became, according to the Spirit, the mother of all his

40. J. Dillersberger, *Das neue Wort über Maria* (Salzburg, 1947), p. 94.
41. St. Maximilian Kolbe, Fragment of his unfinished book on the Immaculata, August 1940, BMK, p. 595.

> members. She it was who through her powerful prayers obtained that the Spirit of our divine Redeemer, already given on the cross, should be bestowed, accompanied by miraculous gifts, on the newly founded Church at Pentecost.[42]

And Pope Saint Pius X writes:

> Moreover it was not only the prerogative of the most holy mother to have furnished the material of his flesh to the only Son of God, Who was to be born with human members, of which material should be prepared the Victim for the salvation of men; but hers was also the office of tending and nourishing that Victim, and at the appointed time presenting him for the sacrifice. Hence that uninterrupted community of life and labors of the son and the mother.... When the supreme hour of the Son came, beside the cross of Jesus there stood Mary his mother, not merely occupied in contemplating the cruel spectacle, but rejoicing 'that her only son was offered for the salvation of mankind, and so entirely participating in his Passion, that if it had been possible she would have gladly borne all the torments that her son bore' (S. Bonaventure 1. Sent. d. 48, ad Litt. dub. 4). And from this community of will and suffering between Christ and Mary she merited to become most worthily the reparatrix of the lost world and dispensatrix of all the gifts that our Savior purchased for us by his death and by his blood.[43]

Benedict XV articulates this even more clearly: "To such extent did she [Mary] suffer and almost die with her suffering and dying son; to such extent did she surrender her maternal rights over her son for man's salvation, and immolated him—insofar as she could—in order to appease the justice of God, that we may rightly say she

42. Encyclical *Mystici Corporis Christi*, paragraph 110

43. Encyclical *Ad Diem Illum*, GWP, p. 132.

redeemed the human race together with Christ."[44]

To Saint Bridget of Sweden the mother of God said:

> Consider, my daughter, the suffering of my son, whose members were to me like my own members and like my heart.... When he suffered, I felt it as though my heart was suffering....When my son was scourged and pierced, my heart was scourged and pierced ...and therefore I boldly dare to say that his pain was my pain, that his heart was my heart. For as Adam and Eve sold the world for an apple, so we, my son and I, bought back the world like being one heart.[45]

Thus the Son accomplishes his mission in the world through his redemptive death on the cross, but only in and with Mary: the Man of Sorrows and the Mother of Sorrows. On Calvary she suffers together with him in her heart everything that he suffers in his body and his soul. As Jesus in his sufferings went to the utmost limit of what was possible, so his mother, in all things like him, suffered in her heart as much as her Immaculate Heart could possibly endure. Saint Bernardine says:

> She remained steadfast by her son as he was dying through her compassion with his death. Unwaveringly she stood beside him, and when the apostles fell away, she continued to stand alone. When Christ had been lifted up on the cross as the sun, the Blessed Virgin stood like the moon at her place, and this stance was sorrowful and full of pain.... and so the Son of God says (*Isa.* 63:3): 'I have trodden the wine press alone, and of the Gentiles there is not a man with me,' but you alone, Mary, have in truth suffered with Me.[46]

44. Apostolic Letter *Inter Sodalicia*, Acta Apostolicae Sedis X, (1918), p. 182. [Cited from Miravalle.]
45. Revelationes Sanctae Birgittae, Lib. 1, ch. 35, in: P. Sträter, *Maria in der Glaubenswissenschaft, op.cit.*, p. 305.
46. *De glorioso nomine Mariae Sermo 1*, in: P. Sträter, *Maria in der Offenbarung* (Paderborn, 1962), p. 295.

The co-Redemptrix

The popes teach that "at the cross Mary sacrificed her maternal rights." A child receives his flesh and blood from his mother; his life is a continuation of the mother's life. His joys and sorrows are the joys and sorrows of the mother. To offend the child means to offend the mother. To do harm to the child means to do harm to the mother. To take the child's life is to take from the mother the meaning of her life. If that is true for every mother, then it is pre-eminently true for the mother of God. All that she was and had, she passed on to her child. She was created exclusively for him: the honor, happiness, and life of her son were infinitely more important to her than her own honor, happiness, and life. To kill him was, for her, something worse than if she herself were to be killed. Now Mary surrendered all this as a burnt offering for the honor of the Father and for our salvation. Two lives, two beings, two hearts are united here in a single sacrificial offering, because her will had merged entirely with his will. Thus there is no redemptive work of Christ without Mary's compassion.

But perhaps we can find an even more profound basis for this mystery. In her compassion, Mary is, as it were, a complement of the Crucified. She allows Christ to expand his sacrifice into her, into the deepest recesses of her soul. Saint Bernard suggests this when he says to Mary, "After Jesus had given up the ghost, the cruel spear that tore open his side clearly did not touch his soul, but it did pierce your heart. For surely his soul was no longer there, but yours could not be torn away."[47] We know, too, that even in his most intense suffering, the higher powers of Christ's soul retained the beatific

47. *Sermo de duodecim stellis [Sermo in dom. infra oct. Assumptionis, 14-15]*, in: *Saint Bernard et Notre Dame* (Sept Fons, 1953), p. 198. [ET in Office of Readings for Sept. 16.]

vision. Mary, however, experienced the mystery of the cross entirely in faith, hope, and love. She is able to present to the High Priest her condition as the sacrifice of an immaculate creature, a condition that he himself cannot experience, because he, the Son of God, is God and as such possesses neither faith nor hope.

Through her complete faith, the deepest component of human intelligence can be sacrificed at the cross. Indeed, through our understanding we can offer to God "reasonable service" or "spiritual worship" (*rationale obsequium*) [*cf. Rom.* 12:1], by living entirely by faith. Mary remains standing beneath the cross and endures, because she possesses perfect faith. To all appearances, everything seems to contradict the promise of the Archangel Gabriel. Christ on the cross is not accepted but rejected by his people, and he is far from ruling over the House of Jacob. But Mary does not argue or doubt and does not seek to understand. In charity she unites herself with the will of the Father. This will is her only light. In her intellect everything is destroyed, everything is sacrificed. Thanks to this total offering of her contemplative faith, Mary can sacrifice to the Father the deepest, most intimate part of her intelligence: a sacrifice that Jesus himself cannot offer. This allows us to perceive the greatness of her compassion. And because Mary is our example and model, in whom we all find our ideal and our perfection, the sacrifice of her understanding, which submits to God's decree in sheer faith, contains also the sacrifice of the understanding of all mankind. In her sacrifice reason is cast into the darkest night and as such is offered up in charity: and this sacrificial offering is precisely what is still lacking in Christ's suffering.

If this is true for reason (through faith), it is just as true for her will, in hope. The deepest desires of the heart of the Immaculata (the honor, happiness, and good of her dearly-beloved son) are offered up to the Father in the mystery of her compassion in an act of complete trust. If we reflect that our consciousness of life is realized in our deepest desires, then we can understand somewhat that through the sacrifice of these desires Mary experienced the most terrible mystical death: death by the sword that pierced the depths of her soul, reaching unto the division of the soul and the spirit [*Heb.* 4:12]. Everything about Mary is slain, offered to her Father in the sacrifice of Jesus himself. Through Mary, all of human nature, along with the most profound and personal things belonging to it, is offered up to the Father for his honor and for the salvation of mankind.

The Mother and Helpmate of the Eternal High Priest

Christ received his human body from Mary. Thus she makes possible his priesthood. He has his vocation from the Father, and the grace of the hypostatic union is his anointing to the priesthood, but without his human nature Christ could not be a priest. Thus she really becomes the mother of Christ's priesthood. She is likewise incorporated into his priesthood through her total self-offering in union with his sacrifice, as well as through her distribution of all his graces to mankind. Saint Albert the Great explains Mary's connection with the priesthood of her son: "The most Blessed Virgin did not receive the sacrament of Holy Orders. But she was full of whatever dignity and grace is conferred through this sacrament. Ecclesiastical dignities are instituted for the purpose of service. The Blessed Virgin, however, was accepted as an assistant in salvation."[48] Since Mary offers

48. *Mariale* Qu. 43, in: P. Sträter, *Maria in der Glaubenswissenschaft op.cit.*, p. 298.

as a sacrifice her maternal rights and her will, which is completely united to her suffering son, she stands beneath the cross as his helpmate, who in fact sacrificed him, as Benedict XV says. And at the moment when he is taken down from the cross and laid on her maternal bosom, Mary offers to the Father the entire priesthood and mediation of Christ. And thereby Mary allows this priesthood to offer up all of human nature to the Father. Christ was already dead when a soldier pierced his side. At the moment when his side was opened, his heart had already stopped beating. The priestly soul of Christ, therefore, was no longer present. Christ was now in the condition of a most pure sacrifice and a mere sacrifice. But beneath the cross stood Mary. Jesus allows her to complete his priesthood, in order to offer him up to the Father in this condition. In this way she completes and perfects Christ's priesthood. She is therefore more than an ordained priest who renews and represents this total sacrifice of the new Adam and the new Eve in the Holy Sacrifice of the Mass. She is, however, involved in this total sacrifice in a unique way, which corresponds exactly to her feminine nature as mother, bride, and helpmate. Certainly, Mary receives everything from him, just as Eve received everything from Adam. But she receives it so as to perfect it, round it out, and complete it, inasmuch as she gives and sacrifices herself and gives and sacrifices him whom she loves more than herself! The Eastern liturgies, too, indicate this when they sing: "O Virgin, who hast freed mankind from the yoke of sin through the cross of thy firstborn son. O my Lady, Blessed Virgin, who hast torn down the dividing wall of hatred through the suffering of thy beloved son: praise be to thee!"[49]

49. Coptic Liturgy, cited in: P. Sträter, *Maria in der Offenbarung* (Paderborn, 1962), p. 129.

Mary's Spiritual Motherhood

Since Mary, the new Eve, stands at Adam's side as his helpmate, dependent upon him yet completely and utterly sharing with him in the redemption of the world, it is also fitting that she should bestow on the world the fruits of redemption—the graces that Christ has won for us—as a mother is entitled to bestow life upon her child. Her spiritual motherhood already has its basis in the fact that Christ is the head and we are the members of his Mystical Body. "Mary is the mother of the whole Christ.... One and the same mother does not give birth to the head without the members nor to the members without the head, for these would be monsters in the order of nature. In the order of grace likewise the head and the members are born of the same mother."[50] Beneath the cross, in the midst of a thousand pangs, Mary gives birth to us, through her union with the new Adam and through her cooperation in his redemptive act, unto the life of grace that belongs to the children of God. The fruits of redemption always come to us through her. With that we have already hinted at the mystery of her mediation of graces, which begins precisely at this point. Saint Thomas Aquinas formulates this truth as follows:

> In every genus, the nearer a thing is to the principle, the greater the part which it has in the effect of that principle.... Now Christ is the principle of grace, authoritatively as to his Godhead, instrumentally as to his humanity.... But the Blessed Virgin Mary was nearest to Christ in his humanity, because he received his human nature from her. Therefore it was due to her to receive a greater fullness of grace than others.... [T]he Blessed Virgin Mary received such a

50. St. Louis Marie de Montfort, *True Devotion*, paragraph 32, p. 13.

> fullness of grace that she was nearest of all to the Author of grace; so that she received within her him who is full of all grace; and by bringing him forth, she, in a manner, dispensed grace to all.[51]

Thus the Immaculata is most intimately united with the sending of the Son into the world. Indeed, Christ's mission to the world, his Incarnation and his redemptive work, are unthinkable without her. It is God's will that we should receive through Mary everything that Christ has done for us. With respect to the sending of the Son, accordingly, we honor her especially as the purest, eternally spotless abode to which God descends—that is the dogma of her perpetual virginity. Above all we honor her as the mother of God, but also as our mother, as the new Eve, as the helpmate of his priesthood and as our co-Redemptrix.

51. *Summa Theologiae* III, q. 27, art. 5.

Chapter Four

The Sending of the Holy Ghost into the World Through the Immaculata

The Father sends not only the Son to redeem the world and bring it back home, but with him the Holy Ghost also. The latter's mission consists of bringing the work of the Son to its completion. He is the gift of the Father and of the Son to the world. This gift enlightens men and "leads them into all truth"; it strengthens them and makes them soldiers and courageous witnesses to Christ; it consoles them and sanctifies them and leads them finally into the depths of God. The Holy Ghost bestows the very love of God upon men and awakens in them a love for God, which he himself is.

The Holy Ghost is entrusted to us by Christ as he is dying on the cross (the spirit, the water, and the blood) and descends into our hearts on the feast of Pentecost. Sacred Scripture, which very rarely speaks about the mother of God, explicitly mentions her presence on that day and gives us to understand that the disciples were gathered around her at the moment when the Holy Ghost descended upon them. Indeed, the Holy Ghost comes to us and thus fulfills his mission only through the Immaculata, which we intend to demonstrate in the following pages. Until the end of time, the Holy Ghost works in the Church as the "Soul of the Church" that fills everything with life and brings it to perfection. The sacred liturgy, the sacraments, and the other institutions of the Church, and also the sanctification of souls and the conferral of graces: all that is the work of the Holy Ghost. The work of the Holy Ghost in its entirety, however, takes place in the Immaculata and through the Immaculata.

The Holy Ghost and the Immaculate Conception

The mission of the Holy Ghost into the world is preeminently visible in the miracle of Mary's Immaculate Conception. In fact the Holy Ghost intimately unites his entire mission with the Immaculata, and so necessarily this union is most profoundly evident at the moment when God calls her into existence and endows her with a nature surpassing that of all other creatures. Who, then, is this maiden, the daughter of Anne and Joachim? Who is this creature, to whom the Archangel Gabriel gives the following names: "Mary", "Full of Grace", "the Lord is with Thee", "Blessed among women"?

Every act of God's love comes from the Father through the Son and the Holy Ghost: the Holy Ghost is the gift of the Father and the Son to the world, a gift containing all of the divine life that has been granted to us. This is profoundly expressed in the hymn *Veni Creator*, which names the Holy Ghost: *altissimi donum Dei*—'O highest gift of the most High'. The Holy Ghost is the personified love of the most Holy Trinity. Now it is a property of the gift to be entirely in the one to whom it is given, just as it is a property of love not to rest until it is entirely in the beloved. The mission of the Holy Ghost consists of this: He is the "fire of love" that desires to bestow divine life in its entirety upon us and to imbue us, so as to divinize us! In what creature will the

Holy Ghost be present most fully? To what creature can he grant his grace most perfectly? To the creature that presents no obstacle to him. With what creature will the Holy Ghost unite himself most profoundly? With the creature that fully accepts his burning love and most ardently returns this love. Such a being is unique, for there is only one human being who never offered him the least resistance, who never hesitated in the least, who is completely open to his prompting and who pleased God immeasurably from all eternity by her boundless humility, purity of heart and love. The Holy Ghost can imbue the soul of this human being with all of his divine life as a grace; with this heart He most intimately unites himself, as much as God can ever unite himself with a creature. Of course, all these prerogatives of this creature are in turn the fruit of that first divine grace of election to the highest summit to which a creature has even been raised: to be the Immaculate Conception.

But what is the deepest possible union between the Holy Ghost and Mary? Saint Maximilian Kolbe had the privilege of penetrating deep into this mystery and will be a reliable guide for us here:

> She is joined in an ineffable manner to the Holy Ghost because she is his spouse; but this is true of her in an incomparably more perfect sense than anything this term can express among creatures. What kind of union is this? It is above all interior; it is the union of her very being with the being of the Holy Ghost. The Holy Ghost dwells in her, lives in her, from the first instant of her existence, and he will do so always, throughout eternity. In what does this life of the Holy Ghost in her consist? He himself is love in her, the love of the Father and the Son, the love by which God loves himself, the love of the entire most Holy Trinity, a fruitful love, a conception. Among created

> resemblances the union of love is the closest. Holy Scripture affirms that 'the two of them become one body' [*Gen.* 2:24], and Jesus insists, 'Thus they are no longer two but one flesh' [*Mt.* 19:6]. In an incomparably more rigorous, more interior, more essential manner the Holy Ghost lives in the soul of the Immaculate, in her very being, and makes her fruitful from the first instant of her existence and throughout her life, that is, forever.[52]

The nature of the union consists in the union of wills. Mary identifies so thoroughly with the will of God that one can speak about a quasi-incarnation[53] of the Holy Ghost in Mary. Saint Maximilian Kolbe always insisted that, of course, there can be no question here of a real incarnation of the Holy Ghost, which would be heretical. Instead he is searching for words and concepts that portray more profoundly the intimate relation between Mary and the Holy Ghost. Therefore the qualifier "quasi" is very important here, so as to make clear that there is only a certain analogy with the mystery of the Incarnation.

> The third person of the most Blessed Trinity was not made flesh. Yet our human word 'spouse' cannot express the reality of the relation between the Immaculata and the Holy Ghost. We can therefore say that the Immaculata is in a certain sense an 'incarnation of the Holy Ghost'. The Holy Ghost, whom we love, is in her, and through her we love the Son. The Holy Ghost is very little appreciated.[54]

We can say likewise that she is the greatest, most excellent, purest temple of the Holy Ghost. Mary herself

52. Final article of February 17, 1941, KR, pp. 211-212.

53. quasi: resembling to some degree

54. Conference dated February 5, 1941, in KMK, p. 428.

corroborates this truth when she defines herself at Lourdes: "I am the Immaculate Conception" and thus assigns to herself the title that in the strict sense is an attribute of God ("I am...") and is applied in particular to the Holy Ghost, who within the Trinity is the eternally perfect, immaculate" conception of the Father and the Son.

If among creatures a bride takes the name of her husband by the fact that she belongs to him, unites herself with him, makes herself like unto him and together with him becomes the source of new life, how much more should the name of the Holy Ghost, 'Immaculate Conception', be the name of her in whom he lives with a love which is fruitful in the entire supernatural economy?[55]

The Holy Ghost willed that she should define in Lourdes her relation to God in this way. Even before she is involved in the mission of the Holy Ghost, she is wedded to him in the closest possible union through her Immaculate Conception. Thanks to this most intimate relation to him she is made capable in the first place and deemed worthy of entering upon her great mission, namely, of being the necessary instrument for the sending of the Son and of the Holy Ghost, of becoming the mother of God, and then the mother of John and of the whole Mystical Body. It is significant that Mary stated her name—"I am the Immaculate Conception"—precisely on March 25, on the Feast of the Incarnation of Christ. On both occasions the Holy Ghost worked the same miracle of fruitfulness: in the production of her own Immaculate Conception and with her in the production of the hypostatic union of the divine Word.

55. Final article of February 17, 1941, KR, 212-213.

He was Made Flesh by the Holy Ghost from the Virgin Mary

Through this first act of sending the Holy Ghost, namely the production of the *Immaculata Conceptio* as his quasi-incarnation, he prepared for himself an instrument through which he would ever thereafter work in the world. Saint Louis Marie de Montfort meditates on this cooperation of the Holy Ghost and the Immaculata:

> God the Holy Ghost ... became fruitful through Mary whom he espoused. It was with her, in her, and of her that he produced his masterpiece, God-made-man, and that he produces every day until the end of the world the members of the body of this adorable head.... It does mean that the Holy Ghost chose to make use of our Blessed Lady, although he had no absolute need of her, in order to become actively fruitful in producing Jesus Christ and his members in her and by her.[56]

In the Holy Ghost, Mary is the source of the Incarnation. The hypostatic union of Christ is the joint work of the Holy Ghost and of Mary. And this work takes place in the inmost being, in the heart of the Immaculata, in her status as spouse of the Holy Ghost, as a conception of the love of Father and Son. Accordingly the fathers of the Church say that Mary first conceived Christ in her heart before he was conceived in her flesh (*prius in mente, quam in corpore*). This spiritual conception of the Word in the Holy Ghost is the source of the hypostatic union. The Holy Ghost is completely and utterly united with Mary, so that Mary acts, as it were, in the person of the Holy Ghost himself and brings about the hypostatic union with him. What does this cooperation consist of? The

56. St. Louis Marie de Montfort, *True Devotion*, paragraphs 20-21, p. 8.

Holy Ghost is the principal cause of the union of the divine and human natures in the Son of God, while Mary is the maternal cause (*causa materna*) of the formation of Christ's body. She is completely and utterly dependent upon the action of the Holy Ghost and her action only prepares the material, so to speak, which the Holy Ghost uses. And yet her action is real, and through charity Mary is one with the Holy Ghost. This loving union allows her to accomplish a work that surpasses her, a work that is infinitely greater than she herself is. In the order of charity there is nothing greater than the accomplishment of a work that is greater than oneself, for charity makes us servants of the one whom we love. Mary is a maidservant, for she acts completely under the influence of the Holy Ghost and thereby accomplishes a work that is greater than she herself is: she becomes the mother of a person who is God. In the order of being there is no greater union than the hypostatic union in Christ, the divine Word that assumes human nature. But in the order of charity there is nothing more precious, worthy, or great than bringing about this very union.

"Spirit, water, and blood" [1 Jn. 5:8] in Light of the Immaculata

The mission of the Holy Ghost at the moment of Christ's redemptive act is especially evident in Saint John, who describes the death of Christ with the words: "And he gave up the ghost." This is more than just saying that Christ breathed his last. What is at stake is an active transfer of the most profound love of God. In his first letter, the Beloved Disciple describes this gift as a revelation of the trinitarian love of God in the triune form of spirit, water, and blood. The Holy Ghost is the love of the Father and of the Son. In Jesus' wounded heart this substantial love of God is revealed: the love of the Father for his dearly-beloved Son, the love of the Son for his Father ("even to death on the cross") and the fruitfulness of this love (the Spirit that proceeds from the wounded heart, as well as the water and the blood that stream forth from the pierced side), the common essence of Father and Son, which is love.

This total love of the Trinity, revealed in the divine heart, now brings forth a most pure fruit. It is the entire fruitfulness of the Holy Ghost himself, which descends into this being and thus renders Christ's redemptive work effective to the utmost degree: from the pierced side of the new Adam comes forth the new Eve. God preordained Mary's Immaculate Conception in anticipation of this moment. Here she is the first of the redeemed, who accepted the grace of redemption into her soul infinitely more than all other human beings taken together. Whereas in all other cases redemption consists in being set free from sins, in her case it consists in preservation from all sin.[57] Thus the Immaculata is the special and most splendid fruit of redemption. Only in this first fruit are there other fruits; only in her and through her are all others redeemed; only in her and through her does God imbue other creatures with his spirit, his water, and his blood. Mary is the *nova creatura* (2 *Cor.* 5:17)—a new creature or the New Creation itself, the perfect image and likeness of God. Her heart is fully and completely immersed in the Love of God, without any distance, interruption, shadow, or hesitation whatsoever. And so she receives the entire fullness of God; she becomes the most perfect icon of God. All this happens in the pierced heart of the new Adam.

57. See Pius IX., Bull *Ineffabilis Deus* (Definition of the Immaculate Conception of the B.V.M.), December 8, 1854.

But what is the mission of the Holy Ghost in this divine plan? In the first creation "the spirit ... moved over the waters"; in the new creation he himself is intrinsically involved in redemption, inasmuch as he becomes, in Jesus and through Jesus, the fountain that springs up into life everlasting. In other words, Jesus' mission in the mystery of redemption consists in the annihilation of sin, reparation, reconciliation, and renewal, whereas the mission of the Holy Ghost consists in the outpouring of divine love into our hearts. The first, most exalted, all-encompassing, exemplary, and prototypical fruit of both missions is the Immaculata. Mary is the great, unique, all-encompassing prize of this love of the three divine persons: through the pierced heart of Jesus, the Father himself sends her this love; the Son forms her into the new Eve; and the Father and the Son cause the love that they share, the Holy Ghost, to become fruitful in her as his bride and quasi-incarnation. Thus the keystone of all creation comes into being, God's masterpiece, the supreme fruit of redemption: the Immaculata, formed out of spirit, water, and blood. In this way the Immaculata becomes the terminus, the full expression of the missions of the Son and of the Holy Ghost in the world.

But how does Mary participate actively and concretely in the mission of the Holy Ghost concerning the work of redemption? Through her compassion. The Holy Ghost is love, and does he not surround the loving deed of the Son with all of his divine essence? Is there any better expression of it than Mary's stance beneath the cross? Mary's heart suffers all the tortures of her son, and that is the greatest possible act of love that a creature could ever be capable of. The new Adam willed not to renew mankind without Mary. The new Adam redeems the world with the new Eve. But what is the action of the new Eve? Loving to the utmost, to the very end! And it is precisely therein that her union with the Holy Ghost becomes apparent.

Christ's suffering (*passio*) is the accomplishment of his mission in the world; Mary's compassion (*compassio*) is the accomplishment of the Holy Ghost's mission in the world. The pierced heart of Jesus is the final consequence and perfection of the hypostatic union, "unto the end". The sorrowful and Immaculate Heart of Mary is the final consequence of her union with the Holy Ghost, the complete outpouring and absolute summit of love. Thus Saint Maximilian can conclude: "In the Holy Ghost's union with her not only does love join these two beings, but the first of the two [the Holy Ghost] is the entire love of the Holy Trinity, while the second [Mary] is the entire love of creation; and thus in this union heaven is joined with earth, all of heaven with all of earth, all uncreated love with all created love; it is the summit of love."[58]

And because Christ Crucified breathes out the Holy Ghost and gives his mother to the world to be our mother, the compassionate Immaculata beneath the cross becomes, in the Holy Ghost, the *Amen* of the hypostatic union, the keystone of Christ's entire redemptive work.

The Holy Ghost and the Immaculata According to Saint Maximilian Kolbe

The mission of the Holy Ghost continues and appears externally in all its fullness since the feast of Pentecost [see *Acts* 2]. In his meditations on the Immaculata, Saint Maximilian Kolbe elaborates especially on this mutual involvement and joint action of the Holy Ghost and the Immaculata. First he recalls the

58. Final article of February 17, 1941, KR, 212.

specific mission of the Holy Ghost in the Church and in souls: "The work of redemption depends immediately upon the second divine person, Jesus Christ, who by his blood reconciled us with the Father, atoned for Adam's sin, and won for us sanctifying grace, along with all sorts of actual graces, and thus the right to enter into the Kingdom of God. Nevertheless the third person of the Holy Trinity also participates in this work. Indeed, the Holy Ghost, in the power of the redemption accomplished by Christ, transforms the souls of men into temples of God. He bestows the adoption of the children of God and makes us heirs to the heavenly kingdom, as Saint Paul says: 'You are washed, you are sanctified, you are justified in the name of our Lord Jesus Christ and of the Spirit of our God' (*1 Cor.* 6:11). By descending into the innermost recesses of our souls, the Holy Ghost, God-Who-is-Love, unites us with the other two divine persons. That is why Saint Paul says in his *Letter to the Romans*: 'We know not what we should pray for as we ought, but the Spirit himself asketh for us with unspeakable groanings' (*Rom.* 8:26). Likewise it says in the *First Letter to the Corinthians* that the distribution of gifts depends on the will of the Holy Ghost (*1 Cor.* 12:8-11)."

Building on this foundation, Saint Kolbe explains that the mission of God into the world must be visible, since we are not angels. The Son himself took on human nature, but the Holy Ghost united himself most intimately with the creature that he had chosen to be his bride: Just as the Son became man in order to show us his boundless love, so too the third divine person, God-Who-is-Love, willed to manifest his mediation between the Father and the Son through a visible sign. This sign is the heart of the Immaculate Virgin, according to the saints who acknowledge Mary as the spouse of the Holy Ghost.... What the Creator said to the serpent concerning the Immaculata—'She shall crush thy head' (*Gen.* 3:15)—must be understood, according to the teaching of theologians, as being valid for all times. Until the end of the ages it is the business of the Holy Ghost to form the elect into new members of the Mystical Body. But as Saint Louis Marie de Montfort demonstrates, this work is accomplished with Mary, in Mary and through Mary. We arrive at this conclusion, namely, that the Holy Ghost works through Mary, with the help of passages from Sacred Scripture and the writings of the saints, who are the best interpreters of Sacred Scripture: 'And I will ask the Father, and he shall give you another Paraclete, that he may abide with you forever: the Spirit of truth' (*Jn.* 14:16-17). 'But the Paraclete, the Holy Ghost, whom the Father will send in my name, he will teach you all things and bring all things to your mind, whatsoever I shall have said to you ...' (*Jn.* 14:26). 'But when he, the Spirit of truth, is come, he will teach you all truth.... he shall glorify Me ...' (*Jn.* 16:13-14). Therefore just as the second divine person appears in his Incarnation as the 'seed of the Woman', so too the Holy Ghost manifests in a visible way his participation in the work of redemption through the Immaculate Virgin. She is, of course, a different person from him, yet is so intimately united with him, that it surpasses our human understanding. Therefore, even though the hypostatic union of the human and the divine in the one person of Christ is a different sort of union, this is by no means opposed to the fact that Mary's action is the very action of the Holy Ghost. For as the spouse of the Holy Ghost, Mary is so highly exalted above all created perfection that she fulfills in everything the will of the Holy Ghost, who dwells in her since the first moment of her conception.

From this union with the Holy Ghost, Saint

Maximilian concludes that Mary is the Mediatrix of All Graces. The Holy Ghost is the fullness of divine life, the Gift of God himself, and has thoroughly imbued his bride with this life. This is the most profound meaning of the Angelic Salutation: *gratia plena*—full of grace, fullness, and totality of grace. Moreover, as the quasi-incarnation of the Holy Ghost, she is indeed nothing other than his own expression, his working *ad extra*. Every gesture of the Immaculata has as its first cause the working of the Holy Ghost. From the foregoing we may conclude that Mary, as the mother of Jesus the Redeemer, became the co-Redemptrix of the human race, and as spouse of the Holy Ghost she participates in the distribution of all graces. So with the theologians we can say: 'As the first Eve through her free action contributed to our ruin and also truly brought it about, so Mary through her free action truly cooperates in the Redemption.'

In order to support this statement, he mentions the great Marian apparitions that he knew about: the manifestation of the Miraculous Medal in Rue dc Bac, Paris, in 1830, and the apparition of the mother of God in Lourdes in 1858.

> Especially in these latter times we comprehend that the Immaculata, the spouse of the Holy Ghost, is our mediatrix. The Immaculate Virgin revealed herself in this way to Sister Catherine Labouré in the year 1830. From statements made by the saint we know that the purpose of Mary's revelations was to declare her Immaculate Conception and her miraculous power with God: 'The most Blessed Virgin turned to look at me and at the same time I heard her voice [saying]: This globe represents all mankind and every individual person. This is the symbol of the graces that I impart to all who call on me. After that an oval frame appeared around the Blessed Virgin, on which was written in gold letters: O Mary, conceived

without sin, pray for us who have recourse to thee. At that moment I heard a voice say: Let a medal be struck according to this image. All who wear it will receive great graces.'

In Lourdes the Immaculate Virgin appeared as Mediatrix: she calls on the sick, the lame, and the infirm to proclaim her holiness and to show our dependence from her in our natural life as well. She gently draws the sin-sick souls to herself, namely unbelievers and sinners with hardened hearts, pours [grace] into their hearts so as to convince them of her power to confer supernatural life upon us.

Finally, three great doctors of the Church are cited to corroborate these realities: "Everything that takes place in Lourdes through the Blessed Virgin Mary confirms the truth of what Saint Peter Damian has said: 'Through the woman the curse spread over the earth; through the Woman blessing was restored to the world,' and also the statement of Saint Augustine: 'Man's fall is the poison that was injected by the woman, and the restoration of man is the salvation that was wrought through the Woman.' Thus Saint Bernard describes what the Immaculata proved through her deeds: 'This is the will of him who wished that we have everything through Mary.'[59]

Every grace for souls comes from the hands of the Mediatrix of All Graces, and not a moment goes by in which she does not grant ever-new graces to each individual soul: graces to enlighten the mind, to strengthen the will, to encourage good deeds, ordinary and extraordinary graces; graces concerning earthly life and graces to sanctify the soul. Only at the Last Judgment and in heaven will we learn how much our dear heavenly mother cares for each soul, for each of her children, so as to conform them to Jesus."[60]

59. *Miles Immaculatae*, No. 1 (1938), BMK, p. 582-585.

60. Fragment of his unfinished book on the Immaculata, August 1940, BMK, p. 596.

The Mediatrix of All Graces—the Realization of the Holy Ghost's Mission

The mission of the Holy Ghost, united with his spouse, the Immaculata, is evident in the Incarnation and in the work of redemption as the mystery of the fruitfulness of his love. This fruitfulness is now expanded and protracted and continues to work in creatures until the end of time through his mediation of graces. This mediation between us and the Son is meant to bridge and overcome the separation that distances us from the loving work of the Son: it is meant to crush the head of the devil and revoke man's alienation from God through sin, to strengthen us in our weakness and inconstancy, to help us rise after the fall, to give us trust in God's mercy, to awaken our faith, strengthen our hope, and enkindle our love.

This mediation of the Holy Ghost occurs now in his spouse who, precisely because she is woman, virgin, and spouse, can become our mother. Here we see how Mary's mediation (and that of the Holy Ghost in her) complements the mediation of the Son. The Son's universal mediation, namely the work of redemption itself, is an objective deed: Christ has suffered for all and atoned for the sins of all. This work is present in the Church in the renewal of his sacrifice on the cross, Holy Mass, and in the sacraments as the sevenfold stream of graces from the fountain of his pierced heart. It is the gift of sanctification (*munus sanctificandi*) that Christ has given to his Church. Similarly Christ has revealed all divine Truth to us and has entrusted this deposit of faith to his representatives on earth (*munus docendi*), who also have the duty to lead men to God in his name (*munus regendi*). Saint Bonaventure, however, says that the mediation of the Son is of course the cause of our sanctification, but not the sole cause. It is completed by the mission of the Holy Ghost. "Without the working in our hearts of the Holy Ghost, who is the love of the Father and the Son and brings us to the Father and the Son, the mission of the Son by the Father and the Son's entire work of redemption would have passed us by uselessly."[61] The German mystical poet Angelus Silesius expresses this truth very simply and profoundly: "If Christ were to be born a thousand times in Bethlehem but not in you, you would still be lost eternally." But the fact that the objective work of redemption penetrates souls, is received (subjectively) by them and bears fruit; is precisely what the Holy Ghost makes possible and brings about. For the mediation of the Holy Ghost opens our hearts to Christ's redemptive work, effects in us the infusion of divine life, *i.e.*, of all graces of conversion and sanctification. All this, however, he accomplishes in the heart of the Immaculata.

> Just as Christ became the source of graces for her, so too the distribution of graces belongs to her. Every grace is the fruit of the life of the Holy Trinity: the Father eternally begets the Son, and the Holy Ghost proceeds from them. By this route every possible perfection in every order flows into the world. Every grace comes from the Father, who eternally begets the Son and grace with a view to the Son. The Holy Ghost, who proceeds eternally from the Father and the Son, forms this grace in the Immaculata and through her he forms souls according to the likeness of the firstborn God-man.[62]
>
> From the moment that this union [of the divine and human natures in the Incarnation] was effected [in Mary's womb], the Holy Ghost grants no grace, the Father does not send down his own supernatural life through the Son and

61. Sent. d. 10, a. 2, q. 2, ad 4, *collationes de septem donis Spiritus Sancti* 1,7.
62. Fragment of his unfinished book on the Immaculata, August 1940, BMK, p. 615.

> the Holy Ghost into the soul except through the Mediatrix of All Graces, the Immaculate, with her cooperation and by her consent. She received all the treasures of grace as her own, and distributes them to whom and in the measure in which she wills. Jesus, Son of God and of man, the God-Man, the mediator between God and man, is the fruit of the love of God and of the Immaculate. As the Son is from all eternity, so to speak, the mediator between the Father and the Holy Ghost, so too Jesus, the incarnate Son, has become the direct mediator between the Father and the Holy Ghost, who is considered in a certain manner as incarnate in the Immaculate, the representative, the spiritual mother of all humanity. And only through her does the love of creatures reach Jesus and through him the Father.[63]

Now Mary's mediation of graces cannot be separated from her own fullness of grace. Instead, the doctors of the Church say that her mediation of graces flows from her fullness of grace as though from a spring, that her own grace overflows upon us all. Saint Bernard writes,

> Who could ever say that she, whom the angel greets as Full of Grace, was unfulfilled? And not only that, but the angel declares furthermore that the Holy Ghost will come upon her. Why do you think that should happen? Of course, solely to bring her a superabundance of grace as well. Since she has already received the Spirit for herself and therefore is personally full of grace, now the same Spirit was to come over her for us also, so that she might become more than full and overflowing with grace. From such fullness we have all received. After all, she is indeed our mediatrix.[64]

63. Final article of February 17, 1941, KR 192.
64. *Sermo 2 in assumptione BMV*, PL 183, p. 396.

Mother of Mercy

We distinguish two sorts of graces that the Holy Ghost unceasingly sends to us through the Immaculata: graces of conversion and of sanctification. Through conversion she draws us out of the perdition of sin and loosens the shackles of the devil, whose head she continually crushes. Through sanctification she gradually leads the soul closer and closer to God and unites it with him. Here we see a most remarkable feature of divine love, which assigns to Mary a special role in bringing the lost son back home to the father:

> God is merciful, infinitely merciful, but he is also just, infinitely just —so much so that he cannot tolerate even the slightest sin and has to demand full reparation for it. The one who distributes the infinite merits of the precious blood of Jesus, which washes these sins away, is the personified divine Mercy in the person of the Immaculata. That is why we rightly call her the Refuge of Sinners, of all sinners, even though their sins are very serious and very numerous. Even when it might seem to them that there was no more mercy left for them. Furthermore, every purification of a soul is for her yet another confirmation of her title, 'Immaculate Conception', and the more entangled in sin the soul was, the more the power of her Immaculate Heart shines forth, inasmuch as she restores to such a soul its snow-white purity.[65]
>
> If someone falls into sin, gives himself over completely to vice, despises God's graces, no longer looks to the good example of others, no longer heeds salutary inspirations, and thus makes himself unworthy of further graces—must such a person give in to despair? No, not at all! For God has given him a mother who observes every one of his thoughts, words, and deeds with a compassionate heart. She does not

65. Commentary on the Act of Consecration, BMK, p. 607.

> look at whether he is worthy of grace or love. She is only the Mother of Mercy, and therefore she hastens, even when she is not called, to the place where the greatest misery prevails in souls. Once she has entered a soul, even if it is as miserable as can be and befouled with sins and vices, she does not allow such a soul to perish, but begs for it the grace of light for the understanding and strength for the will, so that it might come to its senses and get up again. As the Mediatrix of All Graces she cannot and will not obtain the grace of conversion only sporadically, here and there; rather, she wants to give rebirth to all souls.[66]

The whole history of salvation is full of examples of this "intercessory omnipotence" of Mary: spectacular conversions of stubborn unbelievers such as Alphonse Ratisbonne, Paul Claudel, and Léon Bloy, but also less visible graces of conversion in countless souls:

> All conversions start with the Mediatrix of All Graces.... All saints, one could say, are a work of the most Blessed Virgin Mary.... If all souls were able to express themselves, they would produce countless thick volumes giving testimony to the working of the Immaculata, the loving mother of the souls redeemed by the most precious blood of her divine son.[67]

Theology distinguishes between sanctifying grace and actual graces. One particular type of the latter sort is prevenient grace. Before we find ourselves in the state of friendship with God through sanctifying grace, which is the life of God in us, God sends to us, in our misery graces that prepare the soul for this coming of God into the soul. If these prevenient graces did not exist, we would never be capable of accepting divine life within us. And this is precisely the role of the Immaculata. By her prayers she already obtains graces where there is not

66. *Rycerz Niepokalanej*, 4 (1925), p. 131, cited in: O. Domański, *op. cit.*, p. 51.
67. *Ibid.*, p. 52.

yet any sanctifying grace; through her we receive prevenient and preparatory graces. Thus the saintly Church father Germanus says: "No one, O Most Blessed Lady, is filled with the knowledge of God except through thee; no one attains to salvation except through thee; no one receives grace from the divine mercy except through thee."[68]

Now this special love of the Blessed Mother for poor sinners, which we can marvel at in all her apparitions, especially in Fatima, is not just a consequence of her mediation of graces; rather, it involves something else that is very special, which is perhaps the most profound reason why God willed to come to us in precisely this manner, through Mary and only through her. God loves us with an unbounded love and wants to do all that he can to lead us to eternal happiness. But man who is burdened with sins may fear to approach the throne of God. God is light and there is no darkness in him. Darkness cannot exist in his presence. The sinner, however, is full of darkness, full of filth. God's majesty and infinite holiness cannot exist side-by-side with contradiction, rebellion, and denial, namely: sin. That is why sin must be condemned. Christ came into the world to pay for our sins. And despite this act of love, man goes on sinning; participates in the scourging and crucifixion of Christ as the executioners did. Therefore,

> . . . in order that the soul might not lose hope out of fear of God's justice, which sin has offended, God sends the personification of his love, the spouse of the Spirit of maternal love, the Immaculata, who is all-beautiful, spotless, and yet a daughter of man, a sister of human beings. He entrusts to her the administration of his mercy with respect to souls. It is

68. *In dormitione Sanctae Deiparae*, oratio II, Enchiridion Marianum No. 1821.

> similar in our earthly families: in a family the father often rejoices when the mother by her intercession holds back his hand from punishing the child, for then justice is satisfied and mercy can also be displayed. Likewise our heavenly Father, so as not to punish us, gives us a spiritual mother, whose intercession he cannot resist.[69]

Imagine a child that has been very bad and vicious and perhaps has committed many crimes and is rejected by the whole world; would his mother, if she was a good mother, ever disown her child? Wouldn't she beg God all her life long for his conversion, like Saint Monica? And at the slightest sign of remorse in the child, wouldn't she hasten to demonstrate her motherly love for him? And if the child in his despair cried, "Mother", could her heart ever manage to remain deaf to such a cry for help? Who would ever be afraid to go to his mother? Here, though, we have not just any mother, but rather the best of all mothers, whose very nature it is to be the Mother of Mercy. But why did God, in setting out to find sinful man who was lost, decide to give this, his most beautiful and magnificent divine attribute, to a weak creature, to a woman? In order to make the way easy for us, so as to touch our inmost depths, to show us how much he loves us, that he even renounces, as it were, this jewel from his divine crown and so does absolutely everything possible to save us. This is what Saint Bernard meant when he wrote:

> Why should man hesitate to approach Mary in his weakness? There is nothing stern, nothing terrible about her. Everything about her is kindliness, sweetness, gentleness, and mercy. Therefore give thanks to him, who providentially gave you such a mediatrix....[70]

69. Commentary on the Act of Consecration, August 1940, BMK p. 606.
70. *Sermo 2 in Dominica infra Octavo Assumptionis BMV*, PL 183, p. 431.

And that leads us to the most profound reason why God entrusted to her the entire "order of mercy". divine mercy is his loving condescension to the little one, to the insignificant, to our nothingness, to our essential weakness, and (after the Fall) to our misery. God wills to show this, his mercy, to the world. Now this mercy is one among God's many attributes, and therefore it is not possible for us to meditate it in its purity and simplicity. God is mercy; not just mercy, though, but also justice, infinite holiness, etc. Christ, too, who reveals this divine mercy to the world in an incomprehensible way, even unto death upon a cross, reveals the other divine attributes as well: he is, for example, the judge who rewards good and punishes evil. God, however, wants to display mercy in its pure form as mercy alone, and that is why he creates a creature in which his mercy is, so to speak, incarnated, in which is sheer mercy in every fiber of its existence: Mary. She herself is the most beautiful image of the divine mercy: "He hath regarded the humility of his handmaid," and his mercy preserved her even from the stain of original sin. God creates Mary to be completely and radically pure; he wills that she be the object of his mercy, pre-eminently and absolutely, so that we might have a share in this mercy through Mary. Her whole being is the personification of the Holy Ghost, of the personal love of the Trinity. This love, however, shows itself with respect to fallen creatures as infinite mercy that wishes to save, heal, restore, and redeem. Thus Mary is the mercy of God itself among men. This is taught explicitly by Saint Albert the Great. He even says that the name Queen of Mercy is the most appropriate title for Mary's dignity, and that this title, "Mother of Mercy", "Queen of Mercy" can belong to no one else.[71]

71. *Mariale* qu. 75, p. 131, in *Ego Sapientia, La Sagesse qui est Marie* (Laval, 1943), pp. 171-172.

"The miraculous icon of "Our Lady of the Gate of Dawn" is venerated in a chapel on the Eastern Gate of the Lithuanian capital Vilnius under the title "Mother of Mercy". Her face expresses a heavenly peace, a dignity full of majesty, and also a marvelous mildness and motherly love. For many centuries innumerable pilgrims have come to this shrine from all over Central and Eastern Europe."

Chapter Five

God Working in the Church Through the Immaculata

Now God's *actio* in the world through the Immaculata takes place at every point in time, in every place, until the end of the ages. The whole history of the Church is a coming of God to us men through the Immaculata and the return of men to God through the Immaculata. In this chapter we will deal only with the first aspect: how God works in the Church through Mary, how he builds up his kingship through her queenship. Saint Cyril of Alexandria praises the most Blessed Virgin on the feast day of the Annunciation of her divine maternity:

> Praise be to thee, holy mother of God! Through thee the Trinity is honored, through thee the precious cross is celebrated and honored throughout the world. Through thee heaven exults, the angels and archangels rejoice, the demons are terrified, and man is called to heaven. Through thee, the creature immersed in the darkness of idolatry is brought to the knowledge of the truth, and believers have come to holy baptism, and churches are built throughout the earth. Through thy help nations come to repent. What more? Through thee the Son of the one God,

> the true light, has appeared to those who dwell in darkness and the shadow of death. Through thee the prophets have foretold the salvation of the nations and the apostles have preached it.[72]

The fathers of the Church and the saints never tire of giving the most varied titles to the mother of God, in order to praise the powerful role that she plays in the establishment and spread of Christ's kingship on earth. They call her the terror of demons, the destroyer of hell, our protective shield, the world's protection, the health of the Christian people, our sole means of salvation, the healer of human misery, our anchor, our refuge, our intercessor, the patroness of sinners, the return of those who have fallen away....[73]

God's action in the Church until the end of the ages is the spread of the true Faith and life according to his commandments, in keeping with the great commission that Christ gave to his apostles: "Going therefore, teach ye all nations ... teaching them to observe all things whatsoever that I have commanded you" (Mt. 28:18-20). A deeper look into the history of the Church teaches us that the Church's missionary work is most intimately bound up with Mary. She appears as the missionary *par excellence*; her apostolic mission is unique and universal.

The Propagation of the Faith Through the Immaculata

"Rejoice, O Virgin Mary, for thou alone hast vanquished all heresies throughout the world," the Church sings in the Office of the Blessed Virgin Mary. And this has proved true a thousand times over the course of the centuries.

72. *Homilia IV, Enchiridion Marianum* (Rome, 1974), p. 808.

73. See especially the Akathist Hymn, [Eng. ref.].

The Docetists of the first century denied the truth of Christ's humanity. The Church fathers replied, 'Your teaching is wrong, for Christ was born of Mary, who was a human creature like us.' Other heretics rejected Jesus' divinity, and once again the fathers replied: 'You are in error, for Christ was born of a virgin, and only God can be born of a virgin.' Nestorius claimed that there was only a moral union between the two natures in Christ, and consequently he denied the title 'mother of God', since Mary was only the mother of Christ's humanity. The fathers of the Council of Ephesus proved that the title "mother of God" is correct by reaffirming that Christ is one person with two natures. Eutyches taught that after the Incarnation the human nature [of Christ] was absorbed into the divine nature and that only the divine nature remained. To this the defenders of the true Faith answered that Christ is of the same nature as God the Father, but also of the same nature as his mother, who has a purely human nature. Cardinal Newman summarizes this by saying that 'Mary is the guardian of the truth of Christ's Incarnation.' The saints who fought against the erroneous teachings of Protestantism and Jansenism countered the new heresies with these Marian truths (*e.g.*, Francis de Sales, Peter Canisius, Louis Marie Grignion de Montfort), and the peoples who cherished devotion to Mary kept the Faith. Cardinal Newman remarks that the nations that remained faithful to Mary have also preserved the purity of their faith in the divinity of Christ, whereas those who rejected Marian devotion see Christ as little more than a very good man. It is remarkable, too, that the denial of Mary's virginity in a Modernist periodical precipitated the condemnation of this perfidious heresy by the Church hierarchy. Finally, Pope Pius XII views the dogma of the bodily assumption of Mary into heaven as an

> effective means of counteracting materialism and the corruption of morals, besides being a triumph of faith in the supernatural world.[74]

It should not be forgotten either, in this connection, that all religious orders and missionary congregations quite explicitly place themselves under Mary's patronage, because they see in her a guarantee that their religious communities will flourish and expect, through her intercession, heaven's blessing upon their work of spreading the Faith and sanctifying souls. Thus, for example, the founder of the Marists, Fr. Chaminade, says:

> Today the great, prevalent heresy is religious indifferentism, which allows souls to become paralyzed in the stupor of egotism and to be swallowed up by passions. This description of our age, which is sad but true, does not discourage us: far from it! Mary's power has not diminished. We firmly believe that she will vanquish this heresy like all the others, because today as before she is the promised Woman who crushes the head of the serpent, and Jesus Christ teaches us that she is the hope, the joy, the life of the Church and the terror of hell. To her is reserved the great victory for our days. To her belongs the honor of saving the Faith from the shipwreck that threatens us today.[75]

The Immaculata—Help of Christians

The working of God in the Church through the Immaculata can be seen in an especially spectacular way when Mary comes to the help of endangered Christendom and brings about a victory over its enemies despite their overwhelmingly superior strength. The popes themselves have acknowledged over and over again this victory of Mary's, particularly over the Turks, and have introduced special feast days in honor of the

74. E. Neubert, *Marie dans le dogme* (Paris, 1953), pp. 208-210.
75. *Ibid.*, pp. 213-214.

Blessed Virgin on the occasion of various miraculous interventions of the mother of God. In his consecration of the world to the Immaculate Heart of Mary, Pius XII summarizes this faith in Mary's great power and entrusts to her the salvation of the Christian order: she establishes peace for a world at war and peace for souls; she leads those who have gone astray back to Christ's sheepfold; she stops the onslaught of neo-paganism; she brings about the victory of Christ the King.

Her apostolic mission is even more visible in the great Marian movements, which illustrate the workings of the graces of conversion and sanctification obtained through the Immaculata at the level of the general population and public life. Since the beginning of the nineteenth century, Marian sodalities and associations have been springing up everywhere; Pius XII said that they are at the forefront of the lay apostolate.[76] In the year 1954 the "Children of Mary" numbered about 36,000 chapters throughout the world; the most important thing is not the number but rather the fruits of the movement, which have been acknowledged by several popes: the transformation of souls and the grace of purity in so many children and youth. The Legion of Mary, the Militia of the Immaculate, the Blue Army of our Lady of Fatima enlisted many millions of Catholics during the first half of the twentieth century and formed them to take part in an intensive apostolic life through total consecration to Mary. The Church's mission in the world has been so obviously dependent upon Mary, especially in the last two hundred years, that the hierarchy of the Church has not hesitated to speak about "the Age of Mary".

Another sign of this miraculous action of God through the Immaculata is the fact that all great apostles who labored for conversions were great devotees of

76. Papal Bull, "Bis saeculari", *Acta Apostolicae Sedis* 1948, pp. 393-402.

Mary and relied on her completely to bring about the mighty deeds that we marvel at in reading their biographies. The most famous of them are: Saint Bernard of Clairvaux, Saint Albert the Great, Saint Bonaventure, Saint Bernardine of Siena, Saint Lawrence of Brindisi, Saint Francis de Sales, Saint Louis Marie Grignion de Montfort, Saint Alphonsus Liguori, Saint Leonard of Port Maurice, and Saint Maximilian Kolbe. With them are to be numbered the many men of God, founders of congregations, sodalities, and Marian associations, which have renewed entire countries and continents through Mary.

Above all, however, the mother of God accomplishes this divine work in the world through her own personal intervention at thousands of shrines, great and small, throughout the world, which attract large crowds. In this way, especially, the Immaculata appears as the God's prototype and model (*forma Dei*) among men. Pilgrims travel to these havens of grace in order to be formed by her. This formation is nothing other than the loving hand of God, who prepares in our unworthy hearts a place for himself, in which he can place at least a tiny fraction of his graces. In this way her words and actions are impressed upon the hearts of the people who, like children, listen to their mother and imitate her. Thus God can make his way into any mentality, in any place, through Mary, who as it were brings prevenient graces with her in order to prepare people to receive God's sanctifying grace.

At the head of this procession of Mary's direct interventions stand the miraculous apparitions, through which Mary gives vitally important resources to the world so as to prepare the way for God's grace to enter souls. The use of these sensible means corresponds to human nature, which needs the help of visible things in order to perceive and remember what is invisible and to live in accordance with the mysteries of the Faith. Just as someone may have the picture of a person dear to him and might like to look at it, especially when that person is far away, so too the Christian loves the image or the object that reminds him of the presence of Christ and Mary. And so she gives Saint Dominic the rosary, a way of praying that is particularly dear to God; one that communicates to children, through Mary, in brief summary form, the whole mystery of God and instills it in their hearts. To Saint Simon Stock she grants the Scapular of Mount Carmel. The mother clothes her child and thus testifies to her intimate relationship with it. Through this external identification, the child is supposed to resemble the mother interiorly. That is why Mary can promise that whoever wears this garment at the moment of death will not fall into the fires of hell. For she herself will come to drive away the devil, who cannot stain or soil her garment and therefore cannot touch someone who wears this garment so as to cast him into the abyss. In the year 1830 she gives to Saint Catherine Labouré the Miraculous Medal, called "miraculous" because of the countless miracles—conversions and cures—that continue to this day.

Never before had there been in the Church such phenomena, which in a very short time converted entire nations to the true Faith and enkindled a great zeal in souls—more than thousands of saintly missionaries could have accomplished in many years. Through her apparitions on Tepeyac Hill in Mexico, our Lady of Guadalupe converted, in a very short time, the pagan peoples of Central America and has preserved them in the Catholic Faith for centuries down to our time. Lourdes, La Salette, and Fatima are milestones for all Christendom, leading hundreds of thousands back to the Faith in the most difficult times the Church has ever experienced.[77] These great Marian events and the movements that have arisen from them are actually the arena in which the Immaculata works in the hearts of individuals and draws people to her Immaculate Heart and to her son, which is accomplished by a tense struggle for each soul that the Immaculata snatches from Satan.

This fact can be proved by counter examples: when humanity evades the influence of the Immaculata, this sets up an obstacle to God's work in the world. And since God allows man to exercise free will, God's action in the world through Mary (the work of salvation through the Son and the Holy Ghost) is impeded the moment her greatness is obscured or people separate themselves from her. Keeping one's distance from Mary in the name of ecumenism is one of the worst possible affronts to God. In times like these, all Christians have the duty of remaining loyal to their mother, and if they do this, she, the Mediatrix of All Graces who has crushed the head of the serpent, will be for them a "guardian of the Faith".

77. See P. Stehlin, *The Immaculata, Our Ideal* (Angelus Publishing, 2006?), Part 6.

Chapter Six

God's Work at the End of the World Through the Immaculata

Just as the beginning of God's *actio* is the light that shines forth from the darkness, the dawn, the awakening of all things and of all love, so too the end of the *actio Dei* within the world is of particular importance. This is why our Lord and his apostles speak so often and so extensively about the parousia, the second coming of Christ, as the final victory after the terrible battle. And this is precisely where Mary appears in especially radiant glory.

The End of Life

The *actio Dei* in the life of each individual is accomplished at the hour of his death, when God declares an end to his earthly pilgrimage and appears in his presence at the particular judgment as the Judge who will mete out his eternal reward. The prayer of the Church has always emphasized Mary's role at this moment by honoring the Immaculata as the Gate of Heaven and Hope of the Dying. We implore her assistance "at the hour of our death" and ask her to "show unto us the blessed fruit of thy womb, Jesus".

Thus God comes to us as Judge at the most important moment of our existence, in which everything is decided, but he places this moment under the standard of Mary, who reveals her most sublime power at the hour of her child's death and helps to determine the outcome of the particular judgment. This is confirmed by Mary's great promises, which guarantee our eternal salvation if we fulfill her wishes (*e.g.*, to wear the Scapular of Mount Carmel or to practice devotion to her Immaculate Heart, etc.).

If Mary is the Mediatrix of All Graces, then she obtains for us also the greatest and most undeserved grace of final perseverance. Although it is true that for our part no one, not even the holiest saint can merit this grace and therefore no one can ever be sure of his eternal salvation, nevertheless God has deposited this grace in her heart. Indeed, he desires that "all men be saved" and have everlasting life, but he makes this dependent, so to speak, on the presence of the Immaculata at the moment of death. To every human being God offers this final rung of the ladder leading to heaven at the most important moment of existence, precisely in order to prove again and definitively that it is his will that we should receive everything through Mary.

At this decisive moment Mary appears as the personification of all God's mercy and love, who with a glance of her eyes, with a gesture of her hands, with a beat of her heart makes up for all our inadequacies and our unworthiness and makes us pleasing to God. She has this power because she is so intimately united with the Holy Ghost, who works entirely and creatively through her as the "forgiveness of sins itself".[78]

78. *Postcommunio* on the Tuesday in the Octave of Pentecost.

At this moment she also wins the final victory over Satan, whose head she crushes definitively, driving him for ever out of the soul of her dying child. This is the reason why the saints can declare that "a child of Mary is never lost." How important it is, therefore, that we always stay by Mary, in life and in death, for

> . . . wherever you enter, you obtain the grace of conversion and of sanctification, for only through your hands do all graces come to us from the Sacred Heart of Jesus. The Immaculata is our all-powerful intercessor. Every conversion and sanctification is the work of grace, while she is the Mediatrix of All Graces. Therefore she alone suffices to obtain and bestow any grace whatsoever. During the apparition of the Miraculous Medal, Saint Catherine Labouré saw rays darting from the precious rings on the fingers of the Immaculata. These signified the graces that the Immaculata generously grants to those who request them.[79]

In the End Times

In times of the greatest distress, God comes to the aid of the world by sending the Immaculata herself. Through her, his *actio* comes to its full expression, because, except for her, all the other ways that God has of reaching us have been cut off, as it were, by the enemy and the devil has occupied and controls all the bastions. God wills to save mankind, even in the end times. But how can this happen, when man can no longer find God's truth in the confusion of the errors that prevail throughout the world, when he is tempted on all sides to be unfaithful to God and his law and to stray from the path of truth? Through the Immaculata!

79. St. Maximilian Kolbe, *Commentary on the Act of Consecration*, August 1940, BMK, p. 609.

First God reveals to the world the true situation and the great danger through the personal intervention of the Immaculata, especially in her great messages of La Salette[80] and Fatima. Then he sends his graces to the world as the "last means of salvation", concentrating them in the heart of the Immaculata:

> With great longing I desire the spread of the devotion to the Immaculate Heart of Mary, for this heart is the magnet that draws souls to Me, the heart that radiates to the world the streams of my light and my love. It is, finally, the inexhaustible spring from which flows into the world the living water of my mercy.[81]

These words of Christ point very clearly to the events of the end times, as Saint John describes them in the Apocalypse; these events begin with the majestic vision: "A great sign appeared in heaven: A Woman clothed with the sun, and the moon under her feet, and on her head a crown of twelve stars" (*Apoc.* 12:1). Her opponent is Satan, who threatens to destroy her. At Fatima, the Immaculata unfolds these events in the great secret that she revealed to the children on July 13, 1917. This secret, made up of three parts, is nothing less than a Marian application of the final battle described in the Apocalypse.

First the mortal enemy of the Immaculata appears:

> And there was seen another sign in heaven. And behold a great red dragon ... (12:3). And the dragon was angry against the Woman, and went to make war with the rest of her seed, who keep the commandments of God and have the testimony of Jesus Christ (12:17).

80. See below, Part Three, Chapter 6.

81. Letter from Sister Lucia to the Bishop of Gurza dated May 27, 1943, [in:] A. M. Martins, S.J., *Fatima e o Coracao de Maria* (Sao Paolo, 1984), pp. 61-62.

The dragon, who is later referred to as the "old serpent" (12:9), is Satan himself, marked out by God's curse in paradise: "I will put enmities between thee and the Woman, and thy seed and her seed" (*Gen.* 3:15). Since he can do nothing to harm her, he directs all his rage at her children, the souls that he wants to ruin eternally. Therefore, the Immaculata at Fatima also showed the children, in the first secret, the place of this worst possible misfortune:

> We saw something like a sea of fire. Immersed in this fire were the devils and souls, as though they were transparent, black, and orange glowing coals in human form that were swimming in this fire.... The devils could be distinguished from the souls by the horrible and loathsome forms of repulsive, unknown beasts.[82]

Yet immediately after this vision Mary showed God's action. There is a superior way of preserving souls from these fires of hell: "You have seen hell, where the souls of poor sinners go. In order to preserve them from it, God wants to establish in the world devotion to my Immaculate Heart."[83]

The *Book of Revelation* goes on to describe the first helper of the dragon, the beast from the sea.

> And I saw a beast coming up out of the sea, having seven heads and ten horns: and upon his horns, ten diadems: and upon his heads, names of blasphemy .... And the dragon gave him his own strength and great power.... And all the earth was in admiration after the beast. And they adored the dragon which gave power to the beast. And they adored the beast, saying: Who is like to the beast? And who shall be able to fight with him? And there was given to him

82. SLF, p. 172.

83. SLF, p. 176.

> a mouth speaking great things and blasphemies... against God, to blaspheme his name and his tabernacle and them that dwell in heaven. And it was given unto him to make war with the saints and to overcome them. And power was given him over every tribe and people and tongue and nation. And all that dwell upon the earth adored him, whose names are not written in the *Book of Life* of the Lamb which was slain from the beginning of the world.[84]

Exegetes usually interpret these passages in such a way that this beast can only mean a political power.[85]

The second secret of Fatima corresponds to this.

> If my requests are fulfilled, then Russia will be converted and there will be peace. If not, then godless propaganda will spread its errors throughout the world, stirring up wars and persecutions of the Church. The good will be martyred, and the Holy Father will have much to suffer. Many nations will be destroyed.[86]

How can this beast arising from the sea of hellfire, *i.e.*, anti-Christian regimes, be conquered? Through confidence in the Immaculate Heart of Mary and the recognition of her power in public, social, and political life. The expression of this confidence and recognition is consecration to the Immaculate Heart, but especially the consecration of Russia, the land that has become the chief instrument of the gigantic work of destruction accomplished by the beast, which has dragged half the world with it into the pit of communist atheism. This consecration includes conversion to the one truth, first at the individual level, but then also in society and in public institutions and structures, in the Church, among the various peoples, and especially the people of Russia, and finally in the whole world.

84. Apocalypse 13:1-8.
85. See O. Allo, *L'Apocalypse* (Gabalda, 1921), p. 184.
86. SLF, p. 176.

Finally, in the Apocalypse, a second beast appears.

> And I saw another beast coming up out of the earth: and he had two horns, like a lamb: and he spoke as a dragon. And he executed all the power of the former beast in his sight. And he caused the earth and them that dwell therein to adore the first beast.... And he did great signs.... And he seduced them that dwell on the earth, ... saying ... that they should make the image of the beast.[87]

The second beast is a further emanation of the dragon. Three times the Evangelist calls it the "false prophet" (*Apoc.* 16:13, 19:20 and 20:10). Therefore we are dealing here with a power that has the power to prophesy, thus a spiritual, religious power that is in the clutches of evil. This evil is none other than unbelief, which comes "up out of the earth", *i.e.*, from within the Church itself; it superficially imitates Christ's teaching and the Church itself (it had horns similar to the horns of the lamb). In reality, however, this heresy in the Church is inspired by the dragon and is entirely at his service. Whatever one may think about the publication of the third secret of Fatima, there is no longer any doubt as to its essential contents: the almost total destruction of the Church and a heretofore unprecedented number of apostate souls. This is the work of the second beast, which is incarnate, so to speak, in a new world religion that leads entire nations into the great apostasy in the name of a false ecumenism.

Heaven's response, however, is the same: the Immaculate Heart of Mary! In this mystery the response is especially important for the members of the endangered Church itself. Despite his obscure intentions, every offensive of the devil only goes to show even more clearly the greatness of our Lady of Victories. That is why

87. Apocalypse 13:11-14.

heresies develop at first at a dizzying pace: so that at the moment of the worst trial, when it appears that the truth has been crushed irrevocably, the Immaculata will triumph over them all without exception. In this triumphant role of the Vanquisher of All Heresies, the Immaculata appears particularly as the Mediatrix of All Graces of Conversion. As co-Redemptrix she puts an end to the "abomination of desolation in the holy place" and causes the sacrifice of our redemption, the Mass of all times, to illuminate the world once again with its eternal splendor. The Mediatrix of All Graces of Conversion ends the era of false ecumenism. The privileges of her universal motherhood and queenship destroy the cult of humanity, unmask the utopia of the Masonic paradise on earth, and show once again the value of the last things, including especially the unending beauty of the heavenly fatherland. By offering her Immaculate Heart as a "refuge", our Lady of Fatima gives the world the means to overcome even the very worst temptation, namely apostasy from the Faith—a means without which mankind would be completely defenseless against the "demonic wave that is sweeping the world".

Accordingly, the great secret of Fatima portrays the three-dimensional working of Satan, who thereby apes the Holy Trinity. The dragon strives for the ruin of souls. The two beasts are the means of attaining this goal. The first is modern liberalism, embodied in the sects of Freemasonry and in Communism. The second is the new world religion, built on the foundation of false ecumenism. Opposing this monster, in its three embodiments, is the apocalyptic Woman, the Immaculate Heart of Mary. Her "great secret" consists of the fact that she is the one who will crush Satan's head. By fulfilling her will, we can save our souls in a simple way (the promise connected with devotion to the Immaculate

Heart of Mary); renew the Christian world order (connected with the consecration of Russia); and finally rescue the Church (the third secret).

The Immaculata: the Keystone of Divine Revelation

One of the signs of the apocalyptic times is the "great apostasy" with the "abomination of desolation in the holy place". It is the Good Friday of the bride of Christ, namely the complete darkness brought on by the total solar eclipse of divine truth by a new world religion, which systematizes, as it were, all errors and presents them to mankind as a self-contained system. This system is Modernism, which seeks to destroy the true Faith, divine revelation, at its root. In contrast to this apotheosis of all errors and anti-Christian world-views, God wishes the complete disclosure of his truth precisely in these troubled times. The contrast could not be more stark: against the background of the deepest darkness shines forth the light of his revelation most brilliantly, in a twofold manner.

The truth about Mary Concludes and Crowns the Unfolding of all Revelation

Divine truth in its entirety was revealed to us by the time the last of the Apostles died, but most of it implicitly, like a wonderful bouquet of magnificent flowers which for the most part have not yet, or not yet completely, opened up. Now the meaning and purpose of the Church is to unfold this revelation, to make it explicit. Jesus assigns precisely this task to his apostles, headed by Saint Peter, to the teaching Church, and promises her the special assistance of the Holy Ghost, which preserves her from error. This means, however, that the Holy Ghost is promised only so as to unfold what is already present, to make explicit what is implicit, and not to invent something new, which necessarily would not come from Christ and therefore would be contrary to the divine deposit of faith. It would resemble a weed added from outside, which would mar the beauty of the flower garden of divine truths.

Over the course of time one flower after the other opens up under the influence of sunshine and water, *i.e.*, divine grace and the influence of the Holy Ghost. The Holy Ghost, therefore, is this explication of the primary cause, which makes use especially of the following secondary and instrumental causes: the meditations of the saints, the works of the Church fathers, doctors of the Church, and theologians, who analyze the divine mysteries with reason enlightened by faith, and by logical conclusions present these mysteries ever more clearly and distinctly. There are also external influences, in particular the attacks of heretics, who exploit the lack of elaboration and precision in the mysteries in favor of their false interpretations. These provoke a more profound explanation of the revealed truth, one which presents more clearly the object of the revealed doctrine in its causes, in its nature, its corollaries, and consequences.

From the historical perspective, God first reveals the truth about himself (the nature of the Trinity and of each of the three divine persons); then about Christ (Christological dogmas); and about his salvific work (the Church, the sacraments, Holy Mass, the doctrine on grace, the teaching about the Four Last Things). In the process, the mystery of Mary shines forth again and again, but most importantly in order to offer assistance in recognizing the truth about her son. Thus she illumines the truth about Christ, that he is true man, a true son of man, born of a human mother. The dogma of the divine maternity (431) illumines Christ's essence as a single divine person with two different natures which are neither confused with each other nor separated from each other. Her perpetual virginity sheds light on the mystery of the virginal Church, whose prototype she is. All these truths about Mary, as they incidentally become evident over the course of history, have a very discreet character. She wants to remain in the background, so as to give honor to God, according to her mission.

The time comes, however, when God wants to reveal his masterpiece completely, and this is reserved for the end times. In the bouquet of revelation the last, most beautiful flower is saved up for this epoch. Thus the golden age of divine revelation concerning Mary begins with the dogma of the Immaculate Conception in the year 1854. The mystery of her inner being is brought plainly to light (her Immaculate Conception, Virginity, and Assumption into heaven, body and soul). This deeper understanding of her person also helps us to recognize much more clearly her mission. In relation to the person of Christ, she is the mother of God. In relation to his redemptive act, she is the new Eve and co-Redemptrix. With regard to the application of his redemptive act, she is the Mediatrix of All Graces, the Queen and Mother of mankind and the prototype of the Church. In relation to the Holy Ghost, she is the spotless bride, his true faithful instrument, and most sacred temple. Mary, therefore, is the crown, the summit of the revelation of divine truth. In Mary, God has said everything. The purpose of creation is the proclamation, the radiation, the manifestation of God's glory. The purpose of theology as teaching about divine Revelation is the proclamation, the radiation, the manifestation of the entire truth of God. When the whole divine revealed truth has been unfolded and made explicit according to

God's will, when all the flowers in God's garden have opened up and are blooming, then creation (which is outside of God) has done its duty and can come back home to the bosom of the most Holy Trinity.

The Immaculata Causes All of Revelation to Shine Forth Again in a New Light

Something special, however, happens yet again with the opening of this last flower of the divine mysteries: all the truths that had been revealed previously will shine forth again like new in its light. Upon the mysteries of the Faith falls a light that comes from the heart of the Immaculata. When the revealed truths are placed in her light, are brought into relation to her, of course no new thing about them is expressed (*in se*); nevertheless we (*quoad nos*) will perceive them in a hitherto-unknown depth, as much as is at all possible for a creature, because we observe them in the light and with the eyes of her who meditates most deeply and most extensively upon the mysteries of God and who has received the words of the eternal Word utterly and entirely into her heart.

Her relation to the Holy Trinity not only sheds a splendid light on her own mystery, but also on God's inmost being, which is revealed to the greatest extent possible for our meager understanding. In this relation to her, the fatherhood of the Father appears in the most profound light, as well as the generation of the Son, along with the mystery and mission of the Holy Ghost. And in this relation to God she appears as the spotless bride of the Holy Ghost, as the mother of the son and the bridal new Eve of the new Adam, and also as the singular daughter of the Father, and altogether as the most resplendent temple of the Holy Trinity.

We can say the same thing with regard to other

dogmas: through her will shine forth in a special way the mystery of the person of Christ (her motherhood and bridal character) his redemptive work with, in, and for Mary (co-Redemptrix) but also her role in; the Mystical Body (Mediatrix of All Graces, spiritual maternity, queenship); her relation to the sacraments and the Mass; and finally to the Four Last Things.

To whom does God reveal all this depth of knowledge about himself? Only to the understanding of the person who wants to see him in her, and therefore devotes himself completely to Mary, not only so as to belong completely to God, but also in order to know him to the most profound depths possible for a human being. Thus God has willed that we really have all that he could ever give us, everything whatsoever through Mary! "In your light, O Mary, we see divine light" (*in lumine tuo, O Maria, videbimus lumen Dei)*.[88] At Fatima the Immaculata makes this truth clear in a unique way: from her hands and heart streamed a light, a flash, in which the children were able to have a glimpse into the depth of the mystery of the most Holy Trinity, into the realities of heaven and hell.

One might also ask, why this revelation had to wait for the end times? Because this most sublime and most profound insight into the mysteries of God requires the entire deposit of the Faith, as it has been elaborated theologically. When wisdom contemplates things in the light of the highest principles (*altissimas causas*), she uses all the other subordinate reasons and principles that have already been disclosed to the human mind. Thus this Marian insight into revealed truth appears as the synthesis of all theology, further deepened, of course, and exalted by a special grace, namely the gift of the spirit of wisdom, which is precisely the all-surpassing

88. See Psalm 35:12.

insight of Mary herself, which she now wishes to bestow upon her children.

IN THE END MY IMMACULATE HEART WILL TRIUMPH

The latter days come to an end with the definitive victory of Jesus Christ. He, however, does not wish to win this victory without the Immaculata. The great sign that will appear in heaven when Christ comes again to judge the living and the dead will be the glorified cross. Yet we have seen that the cross always consists of the Redeemer and the co-Redemptrix, the Crucified and the Queen of Martyrs, the new Adam and the new Eve.

God's final coming, the last *actio Dei in mundum*, therefore, is the coming of the King, at whose side stands the Queen, the bride of the Lamb:

> I saw a new heaven and a new earth. And I, John, saw the holy city, the new Jerusalem, coming down out of heaven from God, prepared as a bride adorned for her husband. And I heard a great voice from the throne, saying: Behold the tabernacle of God with men (*Apoc.* 21:1-3).

And one of the angels said to the seer: "Come and I will shew thee the bride, the wife of the Lamb. And he took me up in spirit to a great and high mountain: and he shewed me the holy city Jerusalem, coming down out of heaven from God" (*Apoc.* 21:9-10). "And the Spirit and the bride say: Come!" (*Apoc.* 22:17).

Synopsis

The entire *actio* of God upon and within the world occurs at every decisive point with and through the Immaculata. On the divine ladder leading down to us creatures, she is the final step, the reservoir of all graces, the terminus of the missions of the Son and of the Holy Ghost in the world. From this spiritual, honorable, and perfect vessel flows this entire work of God into souls.

If we summarize once again this coming of God in Mary with regard to her specifically, then we see that all of God's work in the world (*ad extra*) is ordained for and directed to the Immaculata. He had her in mind from all eternity as the original plan that he followed in creating the world. In her his entire God-Love shines forth at the moment of her conception as *Immaculata Conceptio*; and through her takes place the conception of his Son, the beginning of his coming into the world; and she becomes the co-Redemptrix through her share in the formation of his human nature (*corredemptrix in esse*). In her takes place the conception of the Church, of all members of his Mystical Body, when she stands beside the new Adam as the new Eve under the cross, and here she becomes the co-Redemptrix participating in his sacrificial act (*corredemptrix in actu*). On the day of Pentecost, the Holy Ghost perfects his union with her, and as his bride and quasi-incarnation she acts, as it were, in his person (*in persona Spiritus Sancti*) in distributing all graces (*omnium gratiarum mediatrix*).

Full of these divine missions, which she embodies, makes present, completes, and extends, she stands there as the great sign in heaven, so as to crush Satan's head to the very end and to triumph over all that is opposed to God through her intercessory omnipotence. At the end of time she appears as the perfect bride who contains within herself the whole redeemed world. She is described as the New Jerusalem, the city build of countless living stones, *i.e.*, her redeemed children. At the end of the world, God's work (*actio Dei*) will reach in her its culmination and perfection, when he gives himself to his children for all eternity in the divine dwelling place that he has prepared, in his "tabernacle of God among men", in his "heaven", in the Immaculata!

Part Three

Creation's Return to God Through the Immaculata

(Reaction Creaturae ad Deum Per Immaculatam)

Introduction to Part Three

God's entire *actio* in our regard, as it was described in Part Two, now encounters creation and invites it to receive into itself this ocean of love and mercy and thus to set out on the way that leads to him. The return to God is the meaning and destination of our existence. In order to reach this destination, we must lay hold of the means that God gives us, so that we will not grow faint along the way and so that we don't fall prey to the enemy. The return to God is a spiritual battle that never ceases as long as we are *in via*—on the way.

Now this return to God takes place along the same way by which he came to us. There is no other ladder to heaven. And just as Mary is the last rung of this ladder descending from God to us, so too she is the first rung of our ascent to God. That is the meaning of the axiom: *per Mariam ad Jesum*—to Jesus through Mary. Saint Anselm explains this in a magnificent prayer:

> Through thee, O glorious Lady, we become worthy to ascend to thy son Jesus, who deigned to descend to us through thee. Through thee, O Blessed Virgin, we can arrive at the glory of him who through thee came to us in our misery.[89]

In this connection Saint Bernard says that in our "travels through this foreign land" we have a "kindly advocate" who precedes us, "who intercedes for us, as the

89. Oratio 54, PL 158, pp. 960-961.

mother of the Judge and the mother of Mercy, with her humble and effective plea in matters of salvation."[90] The Immaculata herself confirms this when she declares at Fatima that her Immaculate Heart is our refuge and the way that leads us to God. Isn't Mary the first creature that returns to God after her Incarnate Son? Yes, she is not only the first, but also encompasses all of us within herself in this progress of union with God. She is the pristine image, the prototype of all the redeemed. Furthermore she is, in certain respects, the representative of all the redeemed, according to the remarkable saying of Saint Thomas Aquinas: "In the Annunciation the Virgin's consent was besought in lieu of that of the entire human nature."[91] Pope Pius XII confirms this with the lapidary comment: In place of all mankind she gave her consent.[92]

The return of the world to God begins in a new covenant of God with mankind. This divine espousal, however, does not take place immediately with mankind as a whole. God chooses to go by way of Mary. There ought to be peace between God and man. Therefore God establishes this covenant, as two powers do when they ratify a peace treaty. Mary is the one chosen by God to represent mankind. Her *fiat* welcomes the eternal Word into the human race. And in her consent, the return (*ractio*, *refluxus*) of all creation to God becomes possible in the first place. In this sense Mary constitutes the beginning of our salvation.[93] How

90. *Sermo Nr 2 in dominica infra Oct. Assumpt. BMV*, PL 183, p. 431.

91. *Summa Theologica* III, q. 30, art. 1.

92. Encyclical *Mystici Corporis*, as cited in: R. Graber, *Die marianischen Weltrundschreiben der Päpste in den letzten hundert Jahren* [henceforth GWP], (Würzburg, 1951), p. 160.

93. See St. Lawrence of Brindisi, *opera omnia*, Pars I (Padua, 1928), cited in: C. Feckes, *Die Heilsgeschichtliche Stellvertretung der Menschheit durch Maria* (Paderborn, 1954) [henceforth FSM], p. 244.

man ought to respond to the *actio Dei* is explained to him not only in God's commandments and in the guidance and instruction of Christ and the Church (objective means of salvation); it is tangibly and vividly set before his eyes in the figure of Mary. Her attitude must become ours; her word—our word; her *fiat*—our *fiat*. Only in the measure that I imitate Mary's consent in my own circumstances will my heart be open to Christ and his grace.

Chapter One

The Beginning of the Return: Total Consecration

In what way, then, does a creature begin his return to God? By an act of his will, a decision, through which a human being takes a step outside of himself, out of self-centeredness, toward his true destination. And since the first rung on the heavenly ladder to God is Mary, this is a step, a decision of the will, toward Mary. If we compare her with a high mountain, upon the summit of which God has settled and from which he comes down to us, then we step up to this mystical Mount Zion and begin to climb the mountain. This beginning, this setting out upon the way to God, is total consecration to Mary. This should not be understood, however, as though Mary were our final destination. We give ourselves completely to Mary as our mother and our Queen, as our way to the final destination, which is Christ. Thereby we do nothing other than imitate Christ himself, who gave himself completely and utterly to Mary. He decided to belong to her as a child belongs to its mother. He has his human body from her alone; he wanted to be completely subject to her during thirty years of his life; he wills to accomplish his work of salvation only with her, and for all eternity he wants to be the son of Mary and to grant all her wishes. Devotion to Mary is therefore an essential component of imitating Christ.

That is why consecration to the Immaculate Heart of Mary is of such great importance in the apparitions at Fatima, why the essence of True Devotion to Mary, according to Saint Louis Marie de Montfort, consists of such a total consecration, that nothing but the word "slave" can describe the right relationship to her. In the *Militia Immaculatae* of Saint Maximilian Kolbe, one becomes a knight of the Immaculata through the act of consecration, in which the "unworthy sinner" asks her to accept him "wholly and completely as her possession and property" and to do with him as she pleases: "with all the faculties of my soul and body, with my whole life, with my death and my whole eternity". Similar explanations can be found in the writings of all the saints who show mankind the way to God.

What does total consecration consist of? First we should distinguish between a consecration to Mary that is merely the expression of a wish, a humble request, and an actual *consecratio*. The first sort of consecration is a legitimate expression of our love for Mary, for example, the prayer, "O my queen and my mother, I am all thine," or a child's consecration to Mary on the occasion of his or her First Holy Communion. The authentic *consecratio*, in contrast, consists in self-giving, in an agreement, to make the gift of self (*donatio*). Through this agreement, one dispossesses oneself and then no longer acts as proprietor and master of his life and actions, but rather as a subordinate who has to conform to our Lady's wishes in everything.

But what happens through this total gift of self? Saint Maximilian Kolbe explains it very clearly: one belongs completely and utterly to her, as her "possession and property". It is the donation not only of what we have, but also of what we are. When Mary says, "I am the Immaculate Conception," then she no longer possesses her being for herself, but is "pure relation to God", being-for-God. Inasmuch as she is completely one with the Holy Ghost, she is completely and utterly consecrated to him, in her inmost being. In just this way we must divest ourselves, down to the depths of our being; the Immaculata must take our whole life in her hands and thus give us to God.

> Complete perfection, to give God the honor that is his due, is based on the fact that we are instruments of The Immaculata, her 'business, her 'property'. Our interior life must be constituted in such a way that we are such an instrument in the hands of the Immaculata, that allows her to guide us in everything. Indeed, we are very weak and we also feel this weakness very often; that is why the only means of getting over this weakness is our consecration to the Immaculata.[94]
>
> One must divest himself of everything as quickly as possible and keep nothing for himself, absolutely nothing. She must do everything; we are only her instruments.... The essential thing is not to do much according to our ideas, but rather to be in her hands. She can accomplish something for the honor and glory of God much better, whereas we botch so many things. Everything depends on our perfect docility with regard to her. There is nothing more perfect than the union of our will with hers.... Only if we uproot from ourselves everything that comes from self and allow the Immaculata to lead us fully and completely, will we reflect her completely in ourselves.[95]

94. Conference dated March 9, 1940, *Konferencje świętego Maksymiliana Marii Kolbego* (Niepokalanów, 1990) [henceforth KMK], p. 371.
95. Conference dated February 17, 1938, KMK, p. 213.

Fr. Kolbe goes even farther.

> We know about possessed persons, through whom Satan thought, spoke, and acted. We want to be even more boundlessly 'possessed' by her, so that she alone thinks, speaks, and acts through us. We want to belong to the Immaculata to such a degree that nothing remains in us that does not belong to her, that we reduce ourselves to nothing, as it were, in becoming hers, that we are transformed into her, that our being is lost in her being, so that only she remains. So that we are as much her own as she is God's own. And she belongs to God to such an extent that she became his own mother. And we, too, desire to become like a mother who bears the Immaculata in all hearts that exist and will ever exist.[96]

Accordingly, we will dispose of our material goods only in dependence upon Mary and use them according to her intentions. We will use our body only according to her wishes. We will voluntarily allow no room to any thought, wish, desire, or idea that the Immaculata would not consent to. Such an attitude, however, can become a habit only if we renew this act of self-giving again and again and keep in it mind.

96. Letter to Fr. Antoni Vivoda dated April 12, 1933, BMK, pp. 259-260.

Chapter Two

The New Law of Life: My Life in the Immaculata

(Maria—forma Dei)

The act of consecration can be compared with the drawing up of a contract. The contract, though, is meaningful only when it is put into practice. Similarly, the day on which two spouses celebrate the sacrament of Matrimony is nothing other than the solemn beginning, the irrevocable promise and the establishment of the indissoluble bond that now unites the two for their whole life. In the same way, total consecration is the solemn beginning, a promise, a new law that must henceforth determine the life one leads. Yet man on earth is subject to the vicissitudes of life, marked by original sin, and therefore he must slowly "become what he is". Now, after the definite decision and choice of the destination and the important act of setting out on the way to that destination, comes the long, wearisome pilgrimage, the daily walk along the way. This journey toward the destination, this daily return home to God, is the realization, the actualization, of the total consecration. There are two aspects to it: a negative movement away from everything that is opposed to this total consecration, and a positive movement toward everything that fosters the realization of this total consecration. In this respect Saint Maximilian is a true disciple of Saint Louis Marie de Montfort, who devotes his entire treatise to this "life in Mary". He says that Mary becomes the divine mold into which we pour the molten material of ourselves, so as to be conformed to Christ in her.

CONVERSION AND THE BATTLE AGAINST SIN

As the Mediatrix of All Graces, Mary first obtains for me the graces of conversion (Refuge of Sinners) and effectively helps me in my daily battle against sin. How does this come about?

Let us take the worst case first: sin already committed. It often happens that a person is so depressed and discouraged about sinning that he no longer rallies and remains lying in the muck. Instead of freeing himself from mortal sin by making an act of perfect contrition, he gives in to the sinister suggestions of the enemy and heaps sin upon sin. Instead of falling just once, the sinner offends God many times, often over a long period of time. That is why it is so important to get up right away, even if one has had a serious fall. "If you fall, don't give in to gloomy sadness, for that is stinking pride. On the contrary, with great love and peace of heart, stand up immediately and keep going! Make amends for the fall by an act of perfect love."[97] If you have had the misfortune of succumbing to temptation,

> . . . then offer yourself to her right away with the whole sorry business of your fall and beg for pardon. 'Dearest Mother, pardon me, and ask Jesus to pardon me, too.' Try to perform your next action in such a way as to give the greatest possible joy to her and to

97. Conference dated April 17, 1934, KMK, p. 59.

> Jesus, and be confident that this act of love will completely wipe out your fault. In your next confession accuse yourself of that fault; but she, Jesus, and the Father will already have forgotten it.[98]

"Do not remain for a single minute in the state of sin, but immediately ask God for forgiveness."[99] Thus the Immaculata comes to the aid of a sinner, even when it seems too late. And instead of offending God a hundred time, he has done so only once. Thus the Immaculata has helped the poor sinner to offend the Lord ninety-nine times less often.

If someone is staunch in fighting sin, the Immaculata hastens to help him even before he falls. As a rule, a sin is preceded by a battle, which may be long or short. How often the faithful testify that, at the moment when they were about to weaken and were already standing at the brink of mortal sin, the mother of God quite miraculously helped them. There are many well-known testimonies of those who wear the Scapular or the Miraculous Medal and declare that, at the moment when it was almost too late, they felt the cloth or the medal on their breast, and that this gave them light to see the terrible thing that they were about to commit.

> Saint Bernard says that we should call on Mary's name in all troubles, dangers, and interior trials. Indeed, we must behave as a child would with its mother. When it sees a danger approaching, it cries, 'Mama, Mama!' and hides in her arms, confident now that nothing bad can happen to it. Our earthly mother cannot deliver us from all dangers, whereas our heavenly mother can and always does save us, if we only call on her for help. One could almost say that this is the secret of quicker sanctification.

98. Fragment of his unfinished book, KR 195.
99. Spiritual Exercises 1912, BMK, p.347.

> The same is true for the times when we fall: we must not become sad, but give everything to the Immaculata, these falls, as her property, so that she can make reparation.[100]

To the extent that we place ourselves in Mary's hands, as we fight against sin, and include her in our spiritual battle, she takes over, so to speak, the direction of our soul and makes us increasingly invulnerable to the attacks of the evil spirit and immune to the smoldering passions within us.

> No temptation is a sin. Even if the temptation lasts a very long time, it is not a sin at all; on the contrary, if the soul resists, it gains merit. As for the method of doing battle: we should not allow doubts and anxiety to make us lose composure, but very calmly give ourselves to the Immaculata and not worry about it, simply have no time for it and busy ourselves with something else.[101]
>
> Do not be surprised if you feel good and evil within yourself. Everything evil comes from you; everything good flows from the hands of the Immaculata, the Mediatrix of All Graces. The evil that we see in ourselves is not all of it; the Immaculata allows us to see only a little so that we do not forget who we are, in and of ourselves. We must fight against our weaknesses, but calmly, and not get angry with ourselves. Place all your trust in the Immaculata alone; then she will guide you. Therefore subject yourself unreservedly to her will and fight on calmly, trusting boundlessly in her, and all weaknesses will be transformed into an even greater good.[102]

100. Conference dated January 14, 1933, KMK, pp. 21-22.
101. Conference dated August 16, 1936, KMK, p. 81.
102. Letter to Brother Mateusz Spolitakiewicz, BMK, p. 280.

Illumination and Sanctification

But this is only the negative aspect. Mary also bestows all the graces of sanctification. As mother she nourishes and trains me; as Queen she strengthens and guides me. The fundamental rule is simple: in order to become holy, we must follow Christ, be conformed to Christ.

> Now what is Mary's role in our sanctification? Through whom did Christ come into the world? Who raised our Lord Jesus Christ? To whom was he obedient? The Blessed Mother raised him. With her own breasts she nursed him; she raised him and underwent many toils and troubles for him. What, then, should we do? Allow the mother of God to raise us after the pattern of Jesus Christ. The saints of all times became holy because the best of all mothers carefully raised them.... As in an earthly family, the father works and toils for the daily bread and the support of the family. But who prepares the daily bread for the children, if not the mother? She distributes the food so that each child receives what best corresponds to his needs. What kind of child would ever say that it didn't like its mother?! It is the same way in the supernatural family. Mary distributes all graces, gives this one to this child, that one to another, in such a way that they correspond precisely to the need of each. Someone who was unwilling to accept these graces would be a very ungrateful child. The devil knows all too well that a soul comes to Christ most easily through the Blessed Mother, and therefore he tries to do everything to keep us from walking this path to Christ. But this is just how the Protestants behave: they honor Jesus, but not the mother of God. They pray the *Our Father* but not the *Hail Mary*. And that is precisely the diabolical way, the way of pride. Subjecting oneself to God—Lucifer

could understand that; but that he, an angel, should subject himself to a human creature—that he could not endure, that was too much of a humiliation.... On the contrary, for us it is the highest honor to have the privilege of serving the holiest, most perfect masterpiece of God.[103]

Saint Louis Marie de Montfort's formula summarizes this clearly and concisely: By doing everything through Mary, with, in, and for Mary, we will accomplish everything perfectly through, with, in, and for Christ. Does that mean that we must constantly be thinking about Mary in order to please Christ?

If we go, for example, into a dining room, we do not think about the tables that stand there. Yet if someone were to ask us whether we expect tables to be standing in a dining room, we would answer him in astonishment that we cannot even imagine a dining room without tables. Likewise we cannot imagine printing *The Knight of the Immaculata* without machines, although few people think about the machines when they have the magazine in their hands. We eat at tables, we sit at the tables, and we do not think about it, for the more self-evident something is, the less we need to emphasize it. In the same way we should not be afraid to pray directly to Jesus, to the Holy Trinity. The more we belong to the mother of God, the more we can do this as a matter of course, because we always have her at our side.[104]

This devotion is by no means something unrealistic or abstract.

Our sanctification does not happen with the passage of years, but rather takes place at every moment. The moment that we have before us will not come again. If it is lived well, then the truth that we have spent

103. Conference dated June 13, 1933, KMK, pp. 36-38.
104. *Ibid.*

it well is true for eternity. And no one can change this. The present moment is in our hands. Often we forget the present moment and linger over what has happened, 'Oh, that person insulted me,' or 'What does that person think about me?', etc. It is just as harmful if we think in an unhealthy way about the future (will I persevere?, etc.). Such thoughts can be a temptation. Only the present moment belongs to us. If our thoughts are somewhere else, then we waste the moment. Instead, we use the moment well if we fulfill God's will in it…just as the Immaculata would use the moment if she were in our position. Let us give it to her, so that we can use the present moment better, so that she may think and act in us. The value of the present moment does not depend on what we will do, but only on how we accomplish this action, for the love of God or out of self-love. We must sanctify ourselves at every moment, for we do not know what the next one will be like. We must sanctify ourselves now, for we do not know whether it will be granted to us to see this evening. The better we fulfill our duties, the better we act for God's honor and the more we correspond to the will of the Immaculata. People say that time is money. Christians say that time is worth as much as the precious blood of Jesus Christ, because our redemption took place in time and we must grow supernaturally in time. Everyone can allow the Immaculata to guide him, and then he will use this moment quite suitably. When the soul begins to make efforts for the present moment, it begins to discover new worlds and priceless thoughts; even an increase in the speed with which duties are fulfilled. And, what is the most important thing of all: the soul begins to be purified, for it strives to stop wriggling out of the hands of the Immaculata.[105]

105. Conference dated January 21, 1939, KMK, pp. 330-331.

Chapter Three

The Reformation of All Departments of Our Life Through the Glories of Mary

In order to gain some understanding of Mary's incomprehensible greatness, we must meditate on the many aspects of her being, her mission, and her life, as well as on the treasures that God has placed within her. Therefore, when we say that Mary is our way to God, that means, concretely, that every aspect of her being has a relation to the corresponding aspect of our being. The glories of Mary are as follows: in her origin and at the foundation of her existence her—Immaculate Conception; in her duty—the divine Maternity; and in her life—the beating of her Immaculate Heart as the channel of all God's graces for the world. The conclusion of her earthly life is defined by the reality of her assumption into heaven, body and soul; her voluntary decisions stand for all eternity under the banner of her queenship. Now if Mary transforms our lives, if she acts in us as the *forma Dei*, remolds, brings forth, nourishes, trains, leads, and guides us and brings us to our destination, then it is as though all her privileges and glories continue in us, permeate and perfect us. Saint Maximilian calls this the practical and social significance of the Marian dogmas.

The Spiritual Foundations of our Existence in Light of the Immaculate Conception

The foundations of our existence are characterized by a twofold reality: first, the supernatural principles of our existence, in answer to the questions: Who am I, why do I exist, what am I for? Then there are the fundamental rules that must define our life concretely in a sinful world, so as to overcome the ravages of original sin. In either case the Immaculata comes to our aid, first to prompt us to build our lives in fact upon this foundation, and then to make us firm, persevering, and consistent in applying these principles. And since the foundations are at the basis, the source, the origin, and beginning of our existence, it is important to bring them into connection with that mystery of Mary which stands at the origin and beginning of her own life: The Immaculate Conception.

Mary, Our Foundation

From the first moment of her existence, Mary is perfect, radiantly pure, immaculate. That means, among other things, that the roots of her being and of her life are completely and utterly in keeping with the divine order, that from the very first moment, her life is unreservedly and absolutely and perfectly directed toward God, that she exists entirely in the truth. The principles that define and guide her whole life are completely permeated by the fact that she is the Immaculata. Psalm 86, which the Church applies to Mary, reminds us of this: "The foundations thereof are the holy mountains: The Lord loveth the gates of Sion above all the tabernacles of Jacob. Glorious things are said of thee, O city of God." Through her union with the Holy Ghost, she can now communicate this status of her being firmly "founded upon the holy mountains" and pass it on to her children. This means that, to the extent that we are close to her, she calls to our minds the true foundations of being, that she gives our lives the harmony and steadfastness that springs from the fidelity and consistency with which we guide our actions according to these principles. Saint Maximilian explains this profoundly:

> Reasonable creatures, in addition, love him consciously and unite themselves to him ever more by means of that love; they return towards him. In addition, the creature entirely filled with this love, with the divinity, is the Immaculate, the one without even the slightest stain of sin, the one who never deviated in any way from the will of God. She is joined in an ineffable manner to the Holy Ghost because she is his spouse; but this is true of her in an incomparably more perfect sense than anything this term can express among creatures. What kind of union is this? It is above all interior; it is the union of her very being with the being of the Holy Ghost. The Holy Ghost dwells in her, lives in her, from the first instant of her existence, and he will do so always, throughout eternity. [...] [T]he return to God, the equal and contrary reaction, takes place by following a path which is the reverse of that of creation. In creation this path begins in the Father and continues through the Son and the Holy Ghost; whereas here, through the Holy Ghost, the Son becomes incarnate in Mary's womb, and in him love goes back to the Father. But she, brought into the love of the Holy Ghost, becomes from the first instant of her existence, and forever and eternally, the 'complement' of the Holy Trinity.[106]

Already in her Immaculate Conception, therefore, Mary becomes the beginning of the return of all creation to God, and she advances along her way to God in untroubled, unspotted, perfect love.

106. Final article of February 17, 1941, KR, 211-212.

> In the Holy Ghost's union with her, not only does love join these two beings, but the first of the two [the Holy Ghost] is the entire love of the Holy Trinity, while the second [Mary] is the entire love of creation; and thus in this union heaven is joined with earth, all of heaven with all of earth, all uncreated love with all created love; it is the summit of love.[107]

The true foundation of the spiritual life consists precisely of this: entirely from God, entirely in God, and entirely to God! Now the Immaculata can convey this foundation to her children.

> At Lourdes the Immaculate Virgin answered Saint Bernadette: 'I am the Immaculate Conception!' With these words she clearly stated that she is not only immaculately conceived, but *is* the Immaculate Conception. In the same way, a thing that is white is something other than whiteness itself, and a perfect thing is something other than perfection itself. When God spoke about himself, he said to Moses, 'I am Who am,' that is, it belongs to my essence that I always have my being from myself, without beginning. In contrast, the Immaculate Virgin has her beginning in God, is a creation, is a conception. Nevertheless she is the Immaculate Conception.[108]

From this, her essential character, as it were, of being-immaculate, she now depicts in order to give us a share in her "immaculate-ness". That means that, in the measure that we devote ourselves to her, she lays in us that magnificent foundation that God laid in her.

Overcoming the Consequences of Original Sin

Our concrete reality, however, looks quite different. Original sin has damaged our human nature at the root and administered to us a poison against which we must

107. *Ibid.*

108. *Miles Immaculatae* No. 1 (1938), BMK, pp. 581-582.

put up resistance as long as we live. Thus we find ourselves in a continual spiritual battle against the enemy. Now it is very hard to keep clearly in mind the conditions of this battle, and even more difficult to order one's life accordingly. Here again the special influence of the *Immaculata Conceptio* is brought to bear. Her working in us is like an unceasing declaration of war against these consequences of original sin. Her proximity enables us to see ever more clearly the poison that has affected us, the possible damage done, and also the remedies without which we would sooner or later fall prey to the enemy. How does she do this? By way of contrast, by placing our fallen reality in the light of her reality. The *Immaculata Conceptio* then makes us aware, on every occasion, of how much we allow ourselves to be guided by our wounded human nature and the extent to which attitudes inspired by sin direct our thoughts, words, and deeds. Thus, for example, we plan our daily routine or even our state in life according to the principles of personal ambition or egotistical, wishful thinking. But then in the light of the Immaculata we very easily discover that the truth is lacking here, the view of reality that sees all as coming from God and returning to God. This results in a battle over principles; without her, we usually emerge as losers, but with her we increasingly prove to be the victors.

The First Foundation: God's Mercy

The Immaculate Conception allows us to recognize one of the most profound principles of our whole existence: divine mercy. In the Immaculate Conception God shows the world who he is in the first place with respect to his creature, and how he wants this fundamental relationship with him to be: it is his entirely merciful condescension to mere nothingness. God grants his love gratuitously, without receiving anything at all in return. Furthermore this grant is God's very first act in our regard, which precedes any possible response on our part. He commits his omnipotence and wisdom in order to grant, without reservation and superabundantly, his love, his light, his happiness, his interior joy. God wills that we exist on the basis of this eternally overflowing gift; he wills to fill us abundantly with his life. Yet he can do this only if we are willing to be receptive, if we are entirely open to his gift. Through sin we have blocked this flow of divine love, and instead of allowing him to grant us his mercy, we imagine that we can take it by ourselves, as though we had a right to these gifts. This is the attitude of pride, which denies God's inmost nature, as well as our inmost nature, and turns it into the opposite. God becomes the servant; man wants to be like God. Now is there any possibility that we can rediscover man as he was actually predestined, as God designed him to be? Is there a human being who has accepted God's mercy so much that he himself has become "pure mercy", according to the beatitude: "Blessed are the merciful for they shall obtain mercy"? The Immaculata! Every fiber of her being is a reflection of God's mercy. She receives everything from him and accepts it, so much so that this divine attribute is, so to speak, incarnate in her. Isn't the creature's response to God's call "Be holy, as God your Father is holy" fatherly and motherly mercy, self-giving, loving concern for the poor and the suffering, without expecting any reward? Isn't this attitude of mercy the proper attitude of love?

Therefore, in the Immaculate Conception we discover anew who God actually is for us and what he wants to be: superabundant gift, the providence of the very best Father, who does not allow his immaculate daughter to be tainted by the slightest evil, who does not allow the evil one to have access to her soul. To the extent that we enter into her attitude of total receptivity, we allow God to be merciful to us again, to grant us superabundant gifts, beginning with the overwhelming gesture of the cleansing of our sins. He never tires of forgiving us again and again, not looking upon our perversity and infidelity, but using even the smallest sign of repentance to immerse us again in his boundless gift of love. Thus he leads us step by step into the genuine relation of the creature to his Creator, in which he realizes in us her immaculateness. Thus Mary becomes the mediatrix of his mercy, the Mother of Mercy. For this reason we understand that, wherever people implore her help, they instinctively know, as a child knows about his loving mother, that she is "merciful", only merciful, full of motherly mercy. And precisely in this way she restores man's relation to God as his first principle and ultimate goal, the Alpha and Omega.

Our Everyday Life Under the Banner of the Immaculate Heart of Mary, i.e., of her Universal Mediation of Graces

God grants us all graces of conversion and sanctification through Mary. We react to this *actio* of God by accepting these graces more and more, by allowing them to come alive and to bear fruit in us. And since God has his graces ready through Mary for every moment, for every situation, for every event and every state and condition of life, we must accomplish this return to God in our everyday life by consciously turning to the Mediatrix of All Graces. This happens when we accept her Immaculate Heart into our lives.

is, according to Saint John Eudes:

> the source and the principle of all her privileges, glories, prerogatives and qualities, which exalt her above all creatures.... It is also the source of all the graces that accompany these qualities, but also the source of all the virtues that she practiced. But why is her heart the source of all this? Because it was the humility, the purity and the love of her heart that made her worthy to become the mother of God and consequently to receive all the other gifts and prerogatives that accompany such an exalted dignity.... We must honor in the Virgin Mary not only certain mysteries and deeds of hers, such as her birth, presentation in the temple, visitation, etc., not only certain qualities of hers, such as her divine maternity, or the fact that she is the daughter of the Father, spouse of the Holy Ghost and temple of the Holy Trinity. We must first and above all honor in her the source and the origin of her holiness and of the dignity of all her mysteries, of all her deeds and personal qualities: and that is her love, for according to the holy doctors of the Church, love is the means of merit and the principle of all sanctity.[109]

Entering into Mary's heart, therefore, is the beginning of life under the banner of love, which is in fact the only way that leads us back to God. Love, as the pattern of all virtues, gives to our whole moral life its value: "At the sunset of our lives we will be judged on our love," says Saint Thérèse of the Child Jesus. Not what we have done and accomplished, but rather how we have done it, *i.e.*, with how much love, will determine the value of our life. Without supernatural love all our moral acts are only "a sounding brass or a tinkling cymbal"

109. Quoted in: J.M. Alonso, *Doctrina y espiritualiadad del mensaje de Fatima* (Madrid, 1990), p. 174.

(*1 Cor.* 13:1), but this love is given to us gratuitously in the heart of the Immaculata; therefore we can increase the value of the acts that we perform in our daily life insofar as we do them in the Immaculate Heart. Thus Mary becomes in the fullest sense "the Mother of Fair Love". This communication of the love of her Immaculate Heart is nothing other than the mediation of all graces, which, indeed, are nothing less than emanations and realizations of the divine love in us.

> Life has value to the extent that it is filled with acts of divine love. Now, our demonstrations of love are full of imperfections. Saint Thérèse was aware that her whole life would be imperfect. Not that she possessed any attachment to these imperfections, but [she knew that] she would always discover new attachments. Now if the soul gives its acts to the Immaculata as her property, then she hands them on to God as her own. In this way our acts of love for God receive all her beauty.[110]

Actual Graces Through the Immaculata

Perfect devotion to Mary according to St. de Montfort and being a knight of the Immaculata according to St. Maximilian Kolbe are nothing other than the willingness and the firm resolution to let the Mediatrix of All Graces work in us completely and without restriction, to permeate every department of our life. And if our Lady of Fatima demanded of the children nothing but "prayer and sacrifice" as the faithful fulfillment of their duties, as devotion in everyday details, in order to console God and to snatch many souls from the danger of eternal punishment, then that is once again only the realization of her mediation of graces. What is it that gives our humdrum daily routine its eternal value, its

110. Saint Maximilian Kolbe, Conference dated November 9, 1940, KMK, p. 413.

co-redemptive power? Supernatural charity, which through Mary permeates our every thought, word, and deed.

If we consider our everyday life in the light of the Catholic doctrine about grace, then we know that, besides sanctifying grace as a state, we also receive various actual graces, "helping" graces, that anticipate a human act, accompany it, and lead it to perfection. If we can describe sanctifying grace as the presence, the life, and the working of Christ in us, and the life of the Holy Trinity with him, then we can fittingly describe actual graces as the presence of the Immaculata, who, after all, is nothing other than, so to speak, the incarnate mission of the Holy Ghost.

Special Actual Graces

How important this aspect is, precisely in our everyday life, which is threatened by thousands of temptations of all sorts! If the unhappy sinner has lost sanctifying grace, or if the Christian who is in a state of grace sees that he experiences setbacks again and again and keeps committing the same sins and errors, then the grace of a new beginning is granted to him again and again through the Immaculate Heart. Her presence guarantees the grace that I can begin anew at every moment. The Immaculata restores genuine joy in life to our contemporary world, which is characterized by hopelessness and anxiety about the future.

> Where the moon, the pregnant symbol of changing fate, is at one's feet, there is no more room for melancholy or the existential experience of 'alienation'. Where the sun becomes one's clothing, the twilight of all doubt and despair is overcome, and where the head of the deadly serpent is crushed, the victorious joy of life must surge after all.[111]

111. Fritz Morgenschweiss, "Marianische Notwendigkeiten", *Seele* (1953), p. 236.

One important aspect of our everyday life is our relationship with our neighbor. We know only too well how much disorder there is in this department. But here, too, the solution is to turn to the Immaculata.

> The soul should turn often to the Immaculata; then it will notice immediately how all disordered attachments begin to weaken. And to the extent that one practices this method, the Immaculata will take one's heart entirely into her possession. Then the soul will love its neighbor, its brethren, with the heart of the Immaculata and strive so that others, too, will devote themselves to her, so that others will also have the happiness that the soul already enjoys now. That will be true, supernatural love of neighbor: holy and angelic, as it is in heaven. Then the earth will become an antechamber of heaven, for this love for God in the Immaculata will not be interrupted by the grave. For this reason we must cultivate and develop love for the Immaculata. We must also come to the help of all our brethren and all people, so that all of them and each individual might become the property of the Immaculata.[112]

Our Mission in Life Under the Banner of the Divine Maternity

The Father sends his Son into the world. The Son's mission is accomplished through Mary, who makes this mission possible through her *fiat*. Mary's divine maternity is her reception of the eternal Word into herself, her carrying of God in her heart and her giving birth to the incarnate Word in the world. It is also the most intimate relationship that there can ever be between persons: the relationship of mother and child. In this sense Mary's divine maternity is the most perfect

112. Conference dated July 4, 1937, KMK, p. 147.

created image, rendering visible the most intimate relationship of the Father and the Son within the most Holy Trinity. In her this is at the same time a spiritual and a fleshly reality: fleshly, since she is physically the mother of God and Christ is flesh of her flesh, blood of her blood; spiritually, since she conceived him "first in her heart, and only then in her body" (*prius in mente quam in corpore*). Since this relationship between God and creature in Mary's divine maternity—the most intimate relationship possible—is the prototype and summit, the meaning and purpose of all God's work, we must conclude that the relationship of our souls to God is nothing other than a copy and a certain participation in this mystery of divine maternity.

Motherhood

If God himself defines the most intimate relationship that he can enter into with a creature as the relationship of a mother to a child, then we can say that every earthly motherhood finds its most profound meaning in reference to the divine maternity: Mary's motherhood is the example and measure of every motherhood on earth, and every motherhood on earth is destined to be an echo of the divine maternity. That means that a mother lives out her motherhood perfectly (and by analogy a father—his fatherhood) when she views it in light of Mary's motherhood. Parents see their child as a gift of God; they see in their child the presence of the divine Child. Conceiving the child and bearing it in the womb become a living reminder and "re-presentation" of Mary's conception of the eternal Word and her bearing of Jesus Christ in her heart. The birth and raising of the child is understood as a divine mission, that is, as the presentation and proclamation of Jesus Christ to the world: bearing Christ in souls. Jesus himself reaffirms such an outlook when he says that whoever does his will is his "brother, sister, and mother".

Mission

Mary's divine maternity helps us to understand in particular the mission that we ourselves have to carry out in our short life. We have to continue the Son's mission in the world; be his instruments so as to lead people home to him, and prepare the way for their eternal happiness. This constitutes a spiritual fatherhood and motherhood with respect to souls, which in a certain way become our children. How do they become our children? By the fact that, through our prayers, our sacrifices, our examples, and the consecration of our lives, we instill Christ in them, communicate Christ's grace, and are instruments of the Immaculata, so that she can bear Christ in souls: and that, indeed, is what constitutes her divine maternity. Every one of us must ask God, "What do you want me to do?" The answer is always: "Be a father and a mother to souls. Imitate the maternity of my mother in your life."

Being a Child of God

Finally, the mother of God trains us in the correct relationship with Christ himself. Here on earth he wishes to be before our eyes a tiny, insignificant child. For that reason he also conceals himself under the unassuming forms of bread and wine. And he wants us to love him as Mary loved him, that is, as a mother loves her child, for there is no more tender relationship of love on earth than the one between mother and child. Of course, we do not mean the merely natural and physical union between them, and certainly not that motherhood that is marred by original sin and often full of egotistical needs. What is "maternal" in our relationship to Christ is the act of entering into Mary's being and taking her maternity as our guide. But how was she the mother of the eternal Son? How did she raise him, live with him, speak with him? Surely the most profound reverence for his majesty was combined here with the deepest possible intimacy of her immaculate love. And to keep this from being something abstract and unreal for us, God gives us a very realistic and intensely-lived analogy: isn't the experience of being a father or a mother one of the most sublime things in human life?

The Presence of God

Our "participation" in and our living under the banner of the divine maternity leads us to the correct understanding of God's presence in us: the true mother lives completely for her child, is entirely devoted to him, sacrifices herself for her child. But this precious jewel, now, is God himself, the incarnate Word. Profound silence, holy peace, and tender recollection characterize Mary's relationship to Jesus. Thus her divine maternity teaches us something that has been almost completely lost in our noisy age: prayer in quiet recollection, living in the presence of God. It has become extraordinarily difficult for us to be quiet. Man flees from quiet and can no longer be silent. Even the spiritual person finds it difficult to maintain inner peace there is so much commotion and noise in his heart. But now he receives into his heart the great mystery; it happens within him as on the day of the Annunciation. God comes into his soul. He now has the privilege of cherishing this mystery and carrying it about within him, as a mother carries her child within her before birth. But since God dwells in us in ineffable silence and grants us his eternal light, the mother must become very quiet and honor the presence of the divine Child within her in profound, reverent silence. Mary's divine maternity becomes the "model" of our life with God.

Our Pilgrimage to God under the Banner of the Queen

The *actio Dei*, understood as the divine reign, the universal and social kingship of Jesus Christ, is accomplished in the triumph of the Immaculata, in her universal queenship. This means that our return to God is clearly defined as the acknowledgment of her queenship, and thus as a continual submission to her will. How does this happen in our daily life?

Queen of All Hearts

Saint Louis Marie de Montfort gives her the title: *Regina cordium*—Queen of all hearts, and thus describes how Mary must rule in us. First it is a rule over our interior life. Indeed, we feel that we are in charge of our interior life. No one may penetrate into the secrets of our heart without our permission: it is the seat of our freedom, of our intimacy, and we alone determine our thoughts, our inclinations, our decisions. In principle we want to submit this interior life to Christ the King, and yet this is extremely difficult for us in our daily routine. In order to make this submission to his will easier for us, he sends us the Immaculata, the Queen who rules in us as a most loving mother. In the measure that we submit our heart and the movements of our heart to her, and abide by her decisions and yield to her will, she becomes Queen of our hearts.

Besides, our interior life is often a riddle even to us. Ignorance, delusion, and distractions prevent us from recognizing clearly the truth about our interior state. This results in uncertainty, doubt, unease, inner discord, and many storms, which often make us lose our sense of direction and even more often paralyze us on the way to

God. Mary's queenship in us gives us that security that a soldier has when he allows himself to be led by an experienced, reliable officer. Or better: the security of a child who relies entirely on its mother's care.

Queen of love

Mary's queenship is a queenship of love. God has given her power over all creatures; without restriction she is their mistress, "terrible as an army set in battle array". Whatever she asks of him is granted to her. She is "the all-powerful intercessor". Yet this omnipotence is utterly and completely in the service of her love: love for God and for her children. In this kingdom there is nothing that does not derive from this love and lead back to this love.

> In her we see nothing imperious, nothing that would bend us down to the dust. Jesus Christ, the God-King, must be worshiped; one must fall prostrate before him in profound humiliation; he is entitled to demand this of his creatures and must do so. Before Mary, however, we stand and kneel in profound reverence, indeed, yet we know that she has been placed by God on our human level so as to perform maternal services for us. She bridges the great distance between her and us by her immense goodness and kindly condescension. She uses her royal power by commanding the powers of nature to serve her, as when she answers prayers, or bids the angels of the spirit world to come to our rescue. Her intercessory omnipotence finds its expression in her mediation of grace. Her thoroughly royal appearance of majesty and splendor serves to capture the very depths of our souls and to draw them aloft to the ideal.[113]

113. P. Sträter S.J., *Maria in der Glaubenswissenschaft* (Paderborn, 1962), p. 347.

Mary's slave

Mary's title as Queen clarifies the meaning of the very important definition of the Christian pilgrim who is returning to God as Mary's "slave" (St. de Montfort), or as Mary's property (St. Maximilian Kolbe). These very forceful expressions indicate the thoroughness with which we must subject ourselves to this Queen, in order to do justice to the reality ordained by God. For we are always in danger of relativizing or restricting this queenship and of excluding it from certain areas of our lives. Saint Louis Marie explains this precisely, when he contrasts the slave with a servant: the latter retains his own will and performs his service only for a certain time and in a certain measure, whereas the former renounces the right to any will whatsoever of his own, and his service is unrestricted in every respect. The servant is also entitled to demand payment for his service, whereas the slave's wage is completely and utterly dependent upon the master's good will. Isn't this title, "slave", exaggerated, or at least, as is often suggested, no longer tolerable in our time?

The most astonishing and moving thing about Mary's queenship is precisely the fact that her relationship to God is exactly the same as our relationship to her. The Queen goes on ahead of us in everything; she not only rules but is also the perfect example. *Ecce ancilla Domini*—Behold, the handmaid, the slave girl of the Lord. No one was so entirely subject to God as she, so much so that God could take possession of her whole being and render her thoroughly "transparent" to God, make her the presence of the Holy Ghost on earth. Furthermore, in this she is only imitating her own divine Son, who "emptied himself, taking the form of a servant, being made in the likeness of men". Her *fiat* is her generous submission and complete consecration of herself without any restriction whatsoever, with no knowledge about her own future. It is the response of perfect love, which completely entrusts itself to the beloved. For this reason the best acknowledgment of Mary's queenship is the imitation of her own slavery with respect to God, the repetition from morning to evening of her *fiat* in all the vicissitudes of our life. We can understand the *Angelus* prayer in this sense as a daily threefold renewal of our consecration to Mary, of our reliance on her will, a declaration of loyalty and submission to her queenship.

The Assumption of Mary, Body and Soul, into Heaven

This dogma about the completion of Mary's earthly life gives to us, on our pilgrim way to God, important information about two realities which appear to be quite different, but which are profoundly connected and rule our lives: first, about the meaning of our bodily life, and second about the purposefulness of our existence. In fact the meaning and life of our body is intimately connected with the goal toward which we ought to strive. Materialism glorifies the body in its present state and promises it happiness here and now, provided that we disregard or even deny the dimension of eternity. The truth of revelation shows the transitory and corruptible nature of the body, but also points toward the goal of life, namely "the resurrection of the body and life everlasting".

The Redemption of the Body

In today's materialistic world the life of the body has become the most important thing, and we cannot retreat from the intense barrage of material things, since we are children of our time. Even if we do not idolize our body, still we have become accustomed to seeking our happiness all too often in the fulfillment of the longings and desires of our body, supposedly so as to attain fulfillment and peace of mind. Pain, sickness, and death show most clearly that these worldly promises are a horrible illusion. And yet man wants his body to be redeemed. This longing is now answered by the dogma of Mary's Assumption into heaven, which invites us to meditate on her glorified body in its unfading, heavenly beauty. Such a glorification is promised for our body also, if only we follow the same path as she did. Because her body was completely and utterly guided by her soul, it was also glorified with that soul. Although the world allows the body to wallow in the lie of naturalism and thus leads mankind into despair and ruin, the knight of the Immaculata, in stark contrast to that, can picture the body as it was predestined to be: immortal.

The Glorified Body

The fulfillment of this longing is not only a solemn promise: it is already a reality. The everlasting beauty of Mary's body in glory gives us both a true appreciation for our body and also an incentive to seize the opportunities to gain a share in that beauty. In the measure that this supernatural reality seizes my imagination and permeates all the departments of my life, I order the life of my body to this reality; refuse to let it fall into illusions and the passions that have been disordered by original sin; and lift it up instead to its true destiny. It becomes a servant of the spiritual life and fulfills its purpose of being a temple of the Holy Ghost. This results in a very positive but always supernatural view of the life of the body and fills man with a perpetual vigor and youthful spirit, which is recalled at the beginning of every Holy Mass: I will go to the altar of God, to God who brings joy to my youth – *ad Deum, qui laetificat juventutem meam* (*Ps.* 42). Then, when the years of old age come and a person has to suffer more and more from the infirmities and disfigurement of his body, this dogma is there as a shining hope that his yearning will soon be fulfilled: the place that the Lord has prepared for us in heaven is not something abstract but is right there before us in the perpetual splendor of the Immaculata taken up to heaven. In her we already see the fulfillment of the Lord's word: "Father, I will that where I am, they also whom thou hast given me may be with me, that they may see my glory which thou hast given me" (*Jn.* 17:24).

A Glimpse of the Goal

Our life is often adrift; we lack the clear sense of direction that ought to permeate our whole routine and direct all our thoughts, words, and deeds toward this overarching goal, like iron filings to a magnet. After all, the final cause in philosophy, the purpose and destination of a thing, is the "cause of causes" (*causa causarum*), which comes at the conclusion when it is realized, yet shapes and orders the entire existence of a thing as its fundamental intention. Now, Mary's Assumption into heaven takes up this place in our lives. Of course, in this regard we should speak first about Christ's Ascension, but Mary's Assumption is closer to us, because Christ, being God, is always with the Father, and his Ascension constitutes the logical conclusion of his mission in the world. In Mary's case, however, this is the final glorification of God's gift of grace to the world and thus most similar to our goal as the perfection of the gifts of grace. Therefore, although in this valley of tears we suffer from the consequences of our exile and are often on the brink of being shattered, the beaming figure of the

Immaculata stands unceasingly before us, as she enters eternity and thus keeps before our eyes the purpose of our whole pilgrimage:

> It must have been a wonderful moment, when Mary arose from the grave with her body glorified by her soul, which was filled with light and grace, and soared aloft to heaven. Since God appointed the angels to the service of men, since the Church prays for everyone whom she carries to the grave: 'May the angels lead you on high with Lazarus to Abraham's bosom,' and since angels were at Mary's side during the major events of her life—the Annunciation and the Birth of her Son in Bethlehem—we can assume that Christ sent whole choirs of angels to greet his mother at the crowning conclusion of her life, to welcome her as queen and to escort her in honor. "What must the holy angels have felt when they saw Mary from afar in her radiant glory? Did they not cry out in astonishment with the choir of virgins, 'Who is she that comes forth like the morning rising, fair as the moon, bright as the sun, terrible as an army set in battle array?' And what answer was given to them? This is the temple of God, the sanctuary of the Holy Ghost, this is the altar of atonement, the ark of the Covenant, the mother of God, the bride of God, the daughter of God, our mother and yours" (Saint Thomas of Villanova, *sermo in festum assumptionis, cap.* 3). But do we really believe that Christ sent only a delegation to greet his mother? If he himself comes to the deathbed of every believer in Holy Viaticum, in order to lead him home, can we not suppose that he himself was present now, at the entrance of his mother, bride, and companion, hastening with the angels to greet her? But who could describe the joy of their encounter, the jubilation of both? What a compensation for the earlier, sorrowful meeting along the way of the cross! Then she was

> alone and abandoned, immersed in a sea of sufferings, brutally torn from the arms of her son; now she is coming up from the desert, overflowing with delights, leaning upon her beloved son (*cf. Cant.* 8:5): this is how Mary goes up to heaven as Queen.[114]

The goal of our life is a participation in this triumph of Mary. Keeping this before our eyes gives us hope and joy in this hopeless, joyless world.

114. O. Cohausz, S.J., *Maria in ihrer Uridee und Wirklichkeit* (Limburg, 1940), p. 226.

Chapter Four

Mediatrix to the One Mediator, Jesus Christ

Jesus Christ is the one mediator between God and men. By his sacrifice on the cross, he reconciled the world with God, and the fruits of his sacrifice are distributed to us in the great means of conveying grace that he himself instituted: his blood, his life, his graces are given to us in the Holy Sacrifice of the Mass and in the sacraments. Now the Immaculata, as the Mediatrix of All Graces, causes this objective mediation of Jesus Christ to reach our souls. This is why Saint Bernard describes her as the channel, the aqueduct. Moreover she disposes our souls and opens doors and gates so that these graces can become effective in us. That is her subjective, maternal mediation, which she carries out in the name and in the power of the Holy Ghost, who works completely and utterly in her and through her. It is the Holy Ghost Who makes her Immaculate-ness a principle, a source in which we all may and must share, if we want to receive divine graces. Thus she prepares the way for Christ:

> We are reborn in Baptism, which takes away our sins. We must be divinized, and for that purpose we have the most Blessed Sacrament.... But how do we prepare ourselves best for these graces? Let us consecrate ourselves to the Immaculata: may she prepare us herself, may she receive her son in us. That is the most perfect means, and the one most pleasing to Jesus, which also communicates to us the most important fruits.[115]

115. Saint Maximilian Kolbe, Conference dated March 23, 1937, KMK, p.112.

In the next section we consider all these great means of salvation in their relation to the Immaculata, so as to understand them more deeply and to allow them to become increasingly real in us: Holy Mass and the sacraments (with the exception of the sacrament of Extreme Unction, which will be mentioned in our consideration of Christian death[116]).

Holy Mass with the Immaculata

Christ's sacrifice is the heart of our holy religion. In order that we may celebrate this sacrifice worthily and share profoundly in it, Christ give us the Immaculata. What is the relationship between Mary and the Holy Sacrifice of the Mass?

Mary's Presence at Holy Mass

The Holy Sacrifice of the Mass is essentially the sacrifice of the cross. But God willed that Mary should share in this Sacrifice on Calvary. As co-Redemptrix she offers to the heavenly Father the same sacrifice as her son, through her renunciation of her maternal rights to him and through the union of her will and her sufferings with the will and the sufferings of Christ. Thus the sacrificial offering of the new Eve constitutes an essential component of the sacrifice on Calvary. It follows that a Mass in which Mary's participation was excluded would no longer fully be the renewal of the sacrifice on Calvary; it would be a mutilated sacrifice! What God has joined, let no man put asunder. In heaven, Mary remains united with her son, Who sacrifices himself upon the altar. She wills the immolation of this sacrificial offering, whose mother she is forevermore.

The Holy Sacrifice of the Mass is the bequest of the merits of the sacrifice of the cross. Mary, however, is the one who distributes all the graces merited on Calvary.

116. See Chapter 7.

Therefore she has a special role at Holy Mass, in which this distribution takes place in an utterly preeminent way. On Calvary Mary gives birth to divine life in us. And this motherhood continues in every Holy Mass: the renewal and re-presentation of the sacrifice of the cross involves the renewal and re-presentation of her mediation of grace.

The graces of the Holy Sacrifice of the Mass are bestowed first and foremost on Mary. She is immaculately conceived in view of the future death of her son (*cf.* The encyclical *Ineffabilis Deus*). The bestowal of Christ's merits on Calvary does not consist now of an increase of graces (since she is, indeed, already full of grace), but rather of an increasing radiance of her glory and of her influence on souls. Thus we pray at the end of the Offertory that God may accept the offering "in honor of the Blessed Mary, ever Virgin". Every Holy Mass brings about the extension of Mary's queenship among men.

Therefore it is legitimate and only right to participate in the celebration of Holy Mass as a kind of standing beneath the cross with Mary, the Mother of Sorrows; as a way of entering spiritually into her sorrowful heart; so as to penetrate with her and in her into the sentiments of our Crucified Lord. Just as she stood discreetly and silently beneath the cross, so she stands discreetly and silently at the altar of sacrifice and allows us in her heart to share in the renewal of the sacrifice of Calvary. Saint John meditated on the tormented Savior on Calvary, and yet he was aware of Mary's presence, and this presence enabled him to understand much more profoundly the mystery of redemption and to love it much more. So it is a mistake to believe that Mary would distract us from meditating on Jesus; on the contrary, she helps us to abide with him more faithfully and to unite ourselves with him more fervently.

For this reason Mary appears again and again during the holy liturgy: in the *Confiteor* she helps us to experience deeper contrition and purity of heart. In the *Credo* we profess her decisive role in the mysteries of the incarnation and redemption. In the prayer *Suscipe Sancta Trinitas,* at the end of the Offertory, we understand the Holy Sacrifice of the Mass as the supreme act of her glorification. In the prayer *Communicantes,* before the words of Consecration, we unite ourselves with her so as to unite ourselves entirely, in her, with Christ's offering. After the *Pater noster* we ask for her intercession, so that the Queen of Peace may bring about in us the peace of Christ. Even the liturgical furnishings are a likeness of Mary, as the Ethiopian liturgy very clearly states when it praises Mary:

> Rejoice, thou golden table, upon which the exquisite mystery ripens. Thou art the golden bowl, in which the manna is kept, the bread that came down to us from heaven. Thou golden paten, which carries the showbread. Thou golden chalice, which contains the wine of the mystery, mixed with the fragrance of the Holy Ghost.... Thou art the golden censer that contains the burning coal of the divinity.[117]

Participating in the Holy Sacrifice of the Mass in the Immaculata.

If we now consider the various parts of the Holy Mass, then the Immaculata is again our guide, who enables us to participate as deeply as possible in this august mystery.

In the first part of Holy Mass we unite ourselves with the Immaculata in her praise and thanksgiving, in

117. Ethiopian Liturgy, Hymn in praise of Mary, in: P. Sträter, S.J., *Maria in der Offenbarung* (Paderborn, 1962), p. 126.

her worship and petition. As the bride of the Lamb, she presents her merits together with our misery to her son. During the reading of the Gospel we recall Christ's words: "My mother and my brethren are they who hear the word of God and do it" (*Lk.* 8:21). In her we are able to "keep all his words in our heart". As the protectress of our faith, she gives our profession of faith its inner strength and constancy.

Mary's role during the Sacrifice of the Mass is symbolized quite expressly by the chalice. She is the pure, golden vessel in which God took up his first dwelling place. The liturgy emphasizes that not only the contents of the chalice are offered, but the chalice itself ("We offer to thee the chalice of salvation...", "the chalice of my blood", etc.), so as to suggest discreetly that the one sacrifice of Christ is nevertheless the sacrifice of Mary as well, that the submission of the new Adam is inseparably united with the submission of the new Eve: that of the Redeemer with that of the co-Redemptrix. We all must place ourselves in this chalice like the little drop of water during the Offertory. As we are assimilated to the qualities of the chalice, we become a worthy vessel of God's presence, filled and imbued with the blood of Christ. A perpetual gaze upon the chalice is an immersion into her Immaculate Heart. Thus we receive into ourselves Christ's loving deed, in all its fullness.

But what are the qualities of the chalice and their meaning for our lives? First, the precious metal in its dazzling beauty: a challenge to cleanse ourselves more and more from every stain of sin, and also from what is worldly and worthless. Then the insight into how precious is our life, our body, and especially our soul, created in God's image and likeness, predestined to share in the beauty of the Immaculata. This chalice, by itself, is quite empty, quite poor. Within it nothing of the world is found, not a speck of dust, nothing worldly, however beautiful it may be. This attitude of complete self-emptying, of complete detachment from self, of total spiritual poverty, is an essential feature of the Immaculata: she has nothing for herself, she does not think about herself, she is completely poor and emptied of self; one might say that her *ego* does not exist. This is the only possible attitude of the creature toward its Creator, when the latter bends down in infinite mercy to our nothingness in order to fill it. Then the chalice is quite open to what is above. The sides of the chalice are like the outspread hands of the *Orate*, full of longing and devotion. This is the virginal heart of Mary, which lives in expectation of God and for God, as totally as a bride for her bridegroom. All her thoughts, words, and deeds are directed toward him, completely for him. Mary gives us this longing for God and makes our hearts become pure of all disordered desires that pull us down.

This longing is fulfilled through consecration and communion. The open heart receives the divine light and the warm, flowing blood of life. This is the purpose for which the chalice exists, and for this alone: that the transformation might take place in it, *i.e.,* that Christ might renew his life, suffering, and death in it. As Blessed Elizabeth of the Trinity puts it so profoundly: "May I be for him an additional humanity, in which he can renew his mystery in its entirety." But this involves the union of one's will with God's will, as completely as Mary was united with Christ in utmost obedience.

Thus Mary is the spiritual space, the holy atmosphere, the sanctuary, in which we are transformed, so as to understand and penetrate ever more deeply into the great divine drama and to receive interiorly all the fruits of this tree of life.

> The heart of Mary is the living altar upon which the sacrifice is offered. This pierced heart is also the server at the altar, whose heartbeat is the liturgical responses. It is the censer, in which the faith, hope, love, and adoration of the whole world ascends like incense before the Lamb who was slain. It is the choir of this formidable Mass, surpassing all the angels. Was not the silence of Mary's wondrous sufferings like the singing of secret, ineffable songs to the enraptured ear of the bloody Victim?[118]

THE LIFE OF BAPTISMAL GRACE THROUGH THE IMMACULATA

In the sacrament of Baptism, untold graces are bestowed upon us; not only must we preserve these graces in our souls, but they have to grow like a mustard seed and become a great tree. We have solemnly promised this through our baptismal vows. But now we find that we are often unfaithful to these vows, that as a result the graces of Baptism cannot shine in us and the indelible mark lies fallow and fruitless, as it were, in our souls. Let us consider the mysteries of the first sacrament in relation to Mary, who after all as our mother gave us supernatural life in Baptism and continually forms and nourishes this divine life in us.

Rebirth.

Baptism is, first and foremost, a rebirth. The death of the old man in Christ's death and a resurrection with Christ. This coming of Christ in the soul is the birth of supernatural life. "The pains of Christ's passion are communicated to the person baptized..., just as if he himself

118. Fr. Faber, cited in: A. Lhoumeau, *La Vie Spirituelle à l'école du Bx Grignion de Montfort* (Paris, 1904), pp. 486-487.

119. St. Thomas Aquinas, *Summa Theologica* III, q. 69, art. 2.

had borne those pains."[119] Now the spell of original sin is broken forever and the prodigal son returns to his father's house. On the cross, the new Adam brought forth a new human race, and we know that he accomplished this only with the new Eve. But now this first baptismal grace continues to work: day by day the remnants of the old man are burned up in Christ's death, but only if the baptized person actively enters into the life, suffering, and death of Christ. And he can do this totally only in Mary, who alone was completely faithful to Christ in his life, suffering, and death.

Baptism bestows sanctifying grace upon us. Through grace the soul is raised to the divine order and participates in God's inmost life. It is the beginning of everlasting life, and one atom of grace is worth more than the whole world. But now this life must grow and be put into practice in the divine family. Mary, as the Mediatrix of All Graces, will tend and preserve in us this greatest of all graces. She especially will help us come to know the divine riches that have been sown in us, of which we are hardly aware. This is what Saint John of the cross means when he exclaims: "O, you souls, created for such glories ... why do you fix your eyes on these trifles, on these vanities?"

Child of God.

Baptism makes us adoptive children of God, brothers and sisters of Christ, full of the Holy Ghost, who continually cries out in our souls, "Abba, Father!" This childhood comes about through the fact that we are "predestinated, to be made conformable to the image of his Son, that he might be the firstborn amongst many brethren" (*Rom.* 8:29). For us personally this means that we can be confident that all the events of our life lead us toward the realization of this conformity with the Son.

Nothing can separate us from this sonship, except our betrayal. Now there is no sonship without a mother. One cannot have God as his Father if one does not have Mary as his mother. Thus devotion to Mary leads us deeper into this sonship; she helps us to make progress and intercedes for us with our heavenly Father.

"If any one love me, he will keep my word. And my Father will love him and we will come to him and make our abode with him" (*Jn.* 14:23). The indelible character of Baptism means that the Father unceasingly sends his Son into the soul, and Father and Son send the Holy Ghost. The entire Holy Trinity continues its interior life of love in the baptized soul, and that is the substance of our greatness and sanctity. But who thinks of this ineffably great reality? Who lives his life within the family of the "Three"? This is possible for us only through the practice of the three supernatural virtues. We live mostly in the banality of worldly realities, on the level of fleeting shadows. The baptismal character is not only a reality but also a constant challenge to live in accordance with this ideal: "Know you not that you are a temple of God and that the Spirit of God dwelleth in you? For the temple of God is holy, which you are" (*1 Cor.* 3:16-17). Mary, whom we may consider as the "blood relation of the Trinity", as the "completion of the Trinity", is there in order to lead us ever deeper into these realities. Through her, indeed, we live in the Trinity. She teaches us how we ought to be temples of God, directed entirely toward him and away from our petty selves. She has allowed the Holy Trinity to work totally in her heart, so much so that the whole mission of the Son and of the Holy Ghost, *ad extra,* has been accomplished in her, and we participate in it only through her. She leads us into the intimate life of the triune God; she trains us to live in these heights.

Through Baptism, indeed, a real friendship begins between the divine persons and the soul. The mother teaches us how a child should behave toward its divine Father. The "friend and blood relation of God" teaches us to become friends of God.

Life in Christ

In an even more concrete way, Baptism means a death of the old man in Christ's death. The Christian is born, suffers, and lives in Christ. He has "put on Christ" (*Gal.* 3:27), is "nailed to the cross" with him (*Gal.* 2:19), and this death is a "falling asleep" in Christ (*1 Cor.* 15:6). In a word: "to me, to live is Christ" (*Phil.* 1:21). All of our life consists of a progressively deeper transformation into Christ. Through Baptism, Christ is the soul of our soul, the life of our life, the principle of our whole supernatural life: we regard and see things as he sees them; we love God and men with his love. Our prayer and sacrifice is immersed in his prayer and in his sacrifice. Now this grace of "being Christ" is actually the gift of the mother, who gives birth to and forms Christ in us. "It is no longer I who live, but Christ who lives in me." But where does Christ live, if not in Mary?

Through Baptism we become members of the Mystical Body of Christ; we enter into the great family of the Church. A new humanity begins, a new life that no longer comes from Adam, but rather from the new Adam and the new Eve. divine life comes from the head and goes to all his members, joins them inseparably with the head and unites them with one another. Thus we are never alone, but have a most intimate relationship with all the members of the Mystical Body, both in the past and also now and in the future until the end of the world. The true Christian never prays only for himself, but for all the members as well, and conversely: all the goods of the entire Church belong to each individual member. We understand our life as a mission, a task within this body. Just as in a human being the eyes see for the whole body, and the tongue speaks in the name of all the members, so too the special task of each one in the Mystical Body is for all, however unassuming and modest it may be. The Immaculata, in turn, actually makes us understand and fulfill this aspect of Baptism. She is, after all, the heart in the Mystical Body, through which all of the supernatural life of the soul (the Holy Ghost) flows to the members. Without her there is no connection with the head; without her there is no union among the members, either. By looking to her we recognize our particular task, our mission, and we also learn to believe in this mission. Who tells me what my calling on earth is, and who gives me a guarantee that I may also carry out this mission? The Immaculata, the channel that causes all the light from the head and from the soul of the Mystical Body to flow into every member.

Glint of Eternity

Baptism is the beginning of eternity, *inchoatio vitae aeternae*. It is the beginning of eternal happiness, making it possible someday to arrive at a destination so full of glory that no eye has ever seen, nor any ear heard, nor has it entered into the heart of man, what God has prepared for those who love him. Often a person can enjoy a little glimpse of these blessings, as we know from the lives of the saints. But as a rule this "seed of eternity" is for us like an ongoing contrast with everyday life. "For the fashion of this world passeth away" (*1 Cor.* 7:31). To live out one's baptismal grace also means to remember this destination always: *et exspecto ... vitam venturi saeculi* (and I look for... the life of the world to come), to feel like a pilgrim and a stranger here on earth and to be increasingly homesick for the eternal fatherland. Every day is a step closer to eternity, a life led to meet the Lord who is to come. The Immaculata, who dwells now entirely in heaven, keeps us aware of this contrast and fills us with the longing for eternity that filled her own heart during her sojourn on earth.

Now in order to revive these graces of the sacrament of Baptism in us through Mary, Saint Louis Marie de Montfort proposes his total consecration to Mary as a slave of love. In the consecration formula he expressly mentions the renewal of one's baptismal vows: "I renew and ratify today through you my baptismal promises. I renounce forever Satan, his empty promises, and his evil designs, and I give myself completely to Jesus Christ, the incarnate Wisdom...." Thus it is extremely helpful to see the magnificent work of "True Devotion to Mary" in light of the baptismal graces that Mary unceasingly renews in us. Thereby the preeminent importance of this sacrament for our life is brought to light again, and through Mary the indelible character begins again to shine throughout our being.

Living the Grace of Confirmation Through the Immaculata

Only through Mary do we receive the Holy Ghost. Indeed, the mission of the Holy Ghost in the world takes place in Mary to such an extent that Saint Maximilian describes her as the quasi-incarnation of the Holy Ghost. But how do we receive the Holy Ghost? First in the sacrament of Baptism, but then especially in the sacrament of Confirmation. The grace of Confirmation gives us the fullness of the gifts of the Holy Ghost, which strengthen our supernatural life and lead us to perfection. Thereby we are enabled to become witnesses and soldiers of Christ. But the fact is that the sacrament of Confirmation often represents a fleeting episode in the life of a maturing Christian, whereas the graces connected with it lie fallow and this great sacrament produces almost no fruit for a great number of people. An indelible character was given to us for all eternity and yet this mark does not shine forth, but is as good as dead in us?! Who can retrieve these hidden treasures, if not the spouse of the Holy Ghost?

Mary was present in the midst of the Apostles when the Holy Ghost descended upon them in tongues of fire. Church art always depicts her in the center, as though to suggest that the tongues of fire of the Holy Ghost spread to the other only through her. The sacrament of Confirmation is "our Pentecost". And living in the indelible character of the Holy Ghost can lead our souls to the summit of sanctity.[120] The first grace of Confirmation is that it enables us to start out on the path to perfection by strengthening our spiritual energies and making us grow "unto a perfect man, unto the measure of the age of the fullness of Christ" (*Eph.* 4:13). The Holy Ghost fills us with the superabundance of his gifts and graces; he strengthens and transforms us, and in a word fulfills his mission, which he began in Mary's womb at the incarnation. Now we know that the Holy Ghost always works entirely through Mary. Accordingly, it is logical that the graces and gifts of the Holy Ghost make me a perfect Christian in the measure in which I place myself under her protective mantle.

The Working of the Holy Ghost in the Immaculata

Through Baptism we became children of God, but then we are like the rough-hewn farm boy who has suddenly been adopted by a royal family. He still feels strange in his new surroundings, doesn't know how to

120. See Leo XIII., Encyclical *Divinum illud munus* dated May 9, 1897 [English ref.].

behave, is clumsy in everything and cannot adapt to his new situation. We have received the most magnificent graces and yet we trudge along wearily and pine away. Therefore God sends us his Holy Ghost in person with his seven gifts. The supernatural virtues planted in us thereby receive new energy from above, which enables them to develop fully. The Church fathers like to draw a comparison with a sail. The virtues are the oars by which we move the boat forward with great effort. The gifts of the Holy Ghost, however, are the sails spread wide, which catch the wind and, at the slightest breeze, enable the boat to travel much faster. Human abilities have been the instruments which the Holy Ghost uses in us. What we do does not change through the gifts, but rather the way in which we act. Through the Holy Ghost our action is no longer merely human (albeit transformed by grace), but divine, that is to say, the work of the Holy Ghost himself, who makes use of our faculties as his instruments. This magnificent divine efficacy of the gifts, though, occurs only if I live in this reality and allow myself to be permeated by this atmosphere. That, in turn, happens only when this reality becomes something quite concrete and understandable in practice. The Holy Ghost himself grants us this concrete reality by becoming quasi-incarnate in the Immaculata and by giving himself to us through her, in the very concrete form of the mediatrix of all his graces. That means that the gifts always begin to have their effect when a person places himself entirely in the hands of the Immaculata as her instrument.

> From the moment that this union (of the divine and human natures in the incarnation) was effected, the Holy Ghost grants no grace, the Father does not send down his own supernatural life through the Son and the Holy Ghost into the soul except through the

> Mediatrix of All Graces, the Immaculate, with her cooperation and by her consent. She received all the treasures of grace as her own, and distributes them to whom and in the measure in which she wills.[121]

In this way the indelible character of the sacrament of Confirmation is applied in a way that is quite concrete. One could say that the "all-too-spiritual" nature of the Holy Ghost, which for us flesh-bound human beings tends to make his efficacy seem remote, abstract, and purely theoretical, now becomes a concrete, visible, and practical reality through his spouse, the Immaculata.

The Seven Gifts of the Holy Ghost in Mary

The spirit of the fear of the Lord causes us to experience God's majesty and our own nothingness. "I AM who am. You are who are not," said God to Saint Catherine of Siena. This gift removes pride from our hearts and allows us to acknowledge our complete helplessness. Thus we recognize that everything comes from God's sheer mercy. And so we no longer rely on ourselves, but rather flee to God and entrust ourselves to him unconditionally. The Immaculata makes this gift blossom in us by placing upon our lips her own canticle of praise: "He that is mighty hath done great things for me, and holy is his name." Her presence in us trains us to repeat her declaration: "Behold the handmaid of the Lord!" Never, not even for a moment, did she think of herself or rely on herself. She was so filled with the All of God and the nothingness of herself that her sole reaction to the most exalted dignity that has ever been conferred upon a creature was to acknowledge God's almighty power and to submit unconditionally and trust in him: ". . .the slave of the Lord—be it done to me according to thy word!"

121. St. Maximilian Kolbe, Fragment of his unfinished book on the Immaculata, August 1940, KR, 192.

The spirit of fortitude makes us courageous and persevering in battle. Mindful of our own weakness, we know what strength we have to count on. "I can do all things in him who strengtheneth me" [*Phil.* 4:13]. The missionary is permeated with this spirit; he is a warrior for the kingdom of God and the salvation of souls, whom no obstacle deters as he journeys to God and leads others along this path. This spirit is manifested in great things and in little, not only in the heroic acts of martyrs and confessors, but also in the "little way". It takes a great heart to avoid becoming banal in the little things. Here again the Immaculata is the best example: every least gesture of her hidden life was full of boundless love for God and souls. Full of devotion and strength she pondered the promise of wise old Simeon, and this same strength kept her standing upright at the foot of the cross. She is not just an example, however; she communicates this strength to us. Aren't her specially chosen servants, the Marian saints, especially filled with the spirit of fortitude, so as to accomplish such great things for her honor and, through her, for the salvation of the world? When a soul devotes itself to her, it receives first and foremost a share in this gift of the Holy Ghost, which impels it to fight in the army of the Immaculata and causes it to persevere in battle and endure to the end.

The spirit of piety enables us to find the right relation to God and to the whole Church. It is the spirit of friendship with God and with our neighbor. It is the relation of the child to its most loving Father and dearest mother, the relation of the brother or sister to the beloved brethren. In the Holy Ghost we have the privilege of praying to God: "Abba, Father!" Everything is full of this profound, fervent affection: our thanks, our petitions, our penance. Through this gift the

Immaculata introduces the uncouth, clumsy child into the family of the Trinity and of the whole Mystical Body and makes it more and more "at home" in these heights.

The way to God is full of steps, both great and small, which all require us to make decisions. The spirit of counsel gives the children of God the instinctive sense to choose at every moment the right path so as to accomplish God's will. But in order to do this, the soul has to pay careful attention to God's prompting. It is the light of the Holy Ghost for every moment, whereby he rarely decides to act by means of sudden inspirations and intuitions, but most often makes use of everyday circumstances and events, through which he makes known his will. Along with all the actual graces that she unceasingly mediates, "Our Lady of Good Counsel" may now give to her knight the grace of a particular light, of good advice as to what should be done at any given moment. When Mary's child earnestly and repeatedly asks, "What would you do in my position?" "How would you decide, mother?" or "What is your will?" then she will surely give the correct answer, the good advice, so that her child may always do what is pleasing to God.

The spirit of knowledge enables us to recognize and sense the "nothingness" of creatures. We must not bind ourselves to any created thing; instead, created things must be a signpost, a help, and a way to God. "The time is short! The fashion [structure] of this world passeth away!" How the saints wept over the lost moments of their lives! But when a human being has loosened the hold of disordered attachments to the "nothingness of creation", then everything becomes transparent and God shines through. Then creation again becomes what it is in God's eyes: God's book, God's sign, the path to God. The Immaculata possesses this spirit in the fullest measure, since she is free from every false tie to a creature, free from even the slightest speck of dust that could mar her soul. Through her presence the spirit of knowledge works in us in such a way that she orders our relation to creatures, puts it right, cleanses and sanctifies it. Only in her is our relationship to others really pure and great and beautiful.

Through the spirit of understanding the soul plunges into the inner life of God himself and perceives and tastes the eternal mysteries more fully. This gift enables us also to see and understand created things, but no longer merely as they are in themselves, but rather as God sees them, through God's eyes from the perspective of eternity. Everything becomes increasingly bright and alive; one's gaze passes through the surface of Sacred Scripture or the liturgy or the teaching of the catechism into the "depths of God" and recognizes more and more of the unfathomable, hidden contents thereof. "But Mary kept all these words, pondering them in her heart." Through this gift the Holy Ghost makes all the mysteries of our Faith shine in a new light by illuminating them with the mystery of Mary. As we have seen, this is the crowning of God's *actio* within the world at the end of the ages.[122]

The spirit of wisdom penetrates into God's inmost nature and makes the soul see the world, in the light of this divine ocean, as a participation in the infinite Good. The soul lives in God and only for God. "I have found heaven within me, for God is heaven, and God is in my soul," exclaimed Blessed Elizabeth of Dijon. Man lives in the *todo* (the All) of God and would like to communicate this "One and All" to the *nada* (the nothingness) of creation. It is a longing for the triumph of Christ's kingship.

122. See Part Two, Ch. 6.

The created wisdom is Mary: Mary's most exalted union with the Holy Ghost is manifested in this gift of wisdom, which draws Mary completely into the depths of God, into the interior life of the most Blessed Trinity. And what does she give to her children? "Now therefore, ye children, hear me. Blessed are they that keep my ways. Hear instruction and be wise, and refuse it not. Blessed is the man that heareth me, and that watcheth daily at my gates, and waiteth at the posts of my doors. He that shall find me, shall find life, and shall have salvation from the Lord" (*Prov.* 8:32-35). Through the gift of wisdom, the heart of the Immaculata, the "Seat of Wisdom", becomes for us the way that leads us to God, into the depths of God himself.

Soldier of Christ—Knight of the Immaculata

The baptized Christian is like a newborn child, which the Church takes into her arms, nourishes, and raises. Through Confirmation the Christian "comes of age", becomes fully grown. Previously he lived, so to speak, only for himself and his own salvation. Now, however, the Holy Ghost is given to him as he once was given to the Apostles, to defend the Faith and all the goods of the Church and to spread them. The confirmed Christian is a witness, an apostle, and a soldier of Christ. For this reason the minister of the sacrament of Confirmation is the bishop as the head of the spiritual army. In the midst of the apostasy of nations and of liberalism, which banishes Christ from modern society, Christ's soldier battles in the power of the Holy Ghost. The love of God impels him to bring the truth and happiness to men, to snatch them away from the errors that poison souls. Thereby each Christian is assigned to his place in the spiritual army; each one has his mission, his specific apostolate. One sees this witness in the young girl who preserves her honor and purity in a filthy world; in a husband and wife who uphold the sacred laws of the family in fidelity in the midst of immorality and dissolution and raise their children in keeping with God's commandments; in the worker who professes his faith without fear of human respect; in the superior who is righteous and is guided by the laws of the Gospel; in the religious men or women who heroically enter the sacred silence of the cloister or selflessly dedicate themselves to works of charity.... Everyone in his station in life is a soldier of Christ in the power of the Holy Ghost.

As beautiful as this may sound, one cannot help raising the objection: the Holy Ghost was bestowed upon all in the superabundance of his gifts, but where is the army of the soldiers of Christ? An objective view shows that these armies were Marian movements, headed by the Legion of Mary, the Blue Army of our Lady of Fatima, and the Militia Immaculatae, along with many other smaller sodalities and Marian religious congregations. This is clear proof that this special grace of Confirmation becomes practically effective once again under the banner of the Immaculata. If we compare the principles of the Militia Immaculatae with this working of the Holy Ghost, we can say that the indelible character of Confirmation first begins to shine and really becomes actuated precisely when the Christian subordinates himself to the general, Mary, in all God's battles and fights in her army. In just this way the Immaculata herself is the quasi-incarnation of the Holy Ghost and makes his efficacy visible exteriorly and palpably, so to speak; thus the Marian armies are the realization and the "incarnation" of the gifts of the Holy Ghost. For this reason we can conclude that just as total consecration to Mary (according to Saint Louis Marie de Montfort) brings the mystery of Baptism closer to home and refreshes and renews in us the graces of Baptism, so, too, the ideal of the Marian Knighthood (according to Saint Maximilian Kolbe, among others) is the actualization and realization of the graces of the sacrament of Confirmation.

Holy Communion in the Immaculata

One of the most beautiful Eucharistic hymns is: *Ave verum Corpus natum de Maria Virgine*—Hail, true body, born of the Virgin Mary! The body of Christ which we receive was formed in the womb of the Immaculata, body from her body, blood from her blood. Without her there would be no Eucharist. Thanksgiving for Holy Communion is therefore always thanksgiving also to her as the first source of this most Blessed Sacrament.

Sacrament of love

Mary is the perfect creature. God did everything for her: for her he created the world, for her first and foremost he became man and sacrificed himself. He instituted the Holy Eucharist firstly for her. Why did He institute this sacrament? Out of love: in order to feed souls in their hunger, in order to console us with his presence during our exile, in order to unite himself completely and utterly with us. Out of love for her, to nourish her in her hunger for God, so that she, too, can feed her children through him. She, more than any other human being ever, suffered from this exile and was consumed with longing for the eternal One. Therefore he wanted to institute his presence in this manner especially for her so as to be most intimately united with her. All the graces that God wanted to enfold in this sacrament Mary first received in her

Communions, and from thence they were to flow into other souls. Therefore the only way that we really and fully receive Holy Communion and the graces and fruits thereof is in her. The Church confirms this when it applies the words of personified Wisdom to Mary: *"Venite, comedite panem meum et bibite vinum quod miscui vobis* — Come and eat my bread and drink the wine that I have mixed for you." She invites us to eat of "her bread", because Christ gave her his eucharistic presence to be her own.

The Mediatrix of the Host.

Based on what we have said, Mary is the mediatrix between us and the Sacred Host. We belong to her entirely and she is spiritually always with us. Therefore, when Christ comes into our soul, he first finds the "Lady of the house" and then he finds us, too, hidden under her protective mantle, in her heart. Her mediation at this moment is of capital importance: here the Almighty continues his act of love to the utmost possibility, humbles himself to take the form of the Host, applies his omnipotence, and accomplishes a whole series of miracles, whereby each one is greater and more significant than even the creation of the whole world. And we receive him with such carelessness, drowsiness, indifference, and distraction! Should we not fear that our declarations of love sound ridiculous and in any case unbelievable, since they are often pronounced with an alarming lack of seriousness? But even if we were to assemble the worship and devotion, the thanks and the love of the saints in this moment, what is that in comparison with Christ's infinite act of love? But now the Immaculata comes into our heart; she loves Christ more than all creatures. Through her union with the Holy Ghost, she is privileged to love Christ with

God's own love. Therefore when we receive him, we can offer Mary to him first of all, and in that way be sure that our wretched heart is most pleasing to him through her presence.

How, then, should and must we receive Holy Communion? We are a bit like a little child that is invited with its mother to a festive banquet. It sees the wonderful things spread out on the table and knows intuitively that everything tastes very good, but has no idea where to begin and doesn't know what foods go together to make a delicious meal. The child can't help itself. It would have no way of telling what the right dishes and the tasty morsels are and would go away from the table hungry, no matter how lavishly it had been spread. Fortunately the mother is there, and she makes the selection, puts the food on a plate, and then feeds the child. So it is with us at the infinitely abundant table of the Eucharist. We are little children in the spiritual life, ignorant and weak. What do we know about the divine nourishment that has been prepared for us? Our position is like that of the Israelites, who were dumfounded by the bread that came down from heaven and asked, "*Man-hu?*"—What is that? We do not know what is best for us. And if we try to serve ourselves, *i.e.,* try to receive the bread from heaven with our own wisdom, then like little children we let the food fall on the floor and spill the expensive drink . . . and walk away from the table hungry and empty! But if Mary is with us, everything is different. She gives us what is best for us and makes sure that the splendid fruits do not fall on the ground. She knows her son and his graces very well, and she knows us very well, too; after all, she is our mother. So we are filled with good thoughts and intuitions, we will love with her heart, and she will worship, give thanks, and make petitions in us. For this reason it is also highly recommended that we pray the *Magnificat* after Holy Communion—Mary's hymn of praise, with which she gave great joy to God on earth and which she continues now in our souls.

Mary's motherly guidance produces in us the best possible disposition for the worthy and fruitful reception of this sacrament. "He who eats my flesh and drinks my blood remains in me and I in him." The purpose of Holy Communion is union with Christ, transformation into Christ. In order to bring this about, the Eucharist is, in the first place, a medicine for our fallen nature, which is self-centered in all things. This egotism is the greatest obstacle, the most serious wound resulting from original sin, and from it all the other weaknesses proceed as from a spring. Now Holy Eucharist first heals this wound of egotism, but only insofar as we prepare ourselves for the reception of its graces. This preparation on our part takes place through acts of self-denial and turning away from the "ego" and turning instead to God, which corresponds precisely to the work that Mary accomplishes in us by instilling the graces of conversion and sanctification.

In her apparitions at Fatima, Mary herself teaches us her importance in our Eucharistic life. The essence of devotion to her Immaculate Heart is the communion of reparation. The notion of reparation is the most important expression of our love as repentant sinners. If I love someone with all my heart and terribly offend him without just cause, then this grieves me more than I can say and I wish that I could undo the wrong. The loving person will make every effort to prove to the offended beloved how sorry he is to have done such a thing to him. He would like to make amends, wipe out with words and deeds the wrong that was done by doing better than ever before. That is reparation! Therefore, if I go to Holy Communion in the spirit of reparation for sins which have been committed against the Immaculate Heart of Mary, then I see myself standing before Christ, Who is the one most affected when someone insults and disparages his dearest mother. I try to console him and for that very reason make reparation for those offenses. That means that Mary guides me into the most profound, the best disposition with which I can receive Christ most worthily. At Fatima, the Immaculata indicates the way that leads us to God, and this way is nothing other than a more profound understanding of the means of grace that Christ himself has given us. Just as Saint de Montfort has us revive the graces of Baptism through Mary, and Saint Maximilian Kolbe—the graces of Confirmation, so Mary herself at Fatima leads us into the utmost depths of the mystery of all mysteries on earth, namely that of union with God in Holy Communion.

Confession in the Spirit of Reparation

Another component of devotion to the Immaculate Heart of Mary is the sacrament of Penance, received in that same spirit of reparation. Now what is Mary's role in making a good confession?

Here, too, she prepares in us the best disposition, awakens in us an increasingly perfect contrition. The more something dirty is brought to light, the more one notices the dirt. The closer I bring my sinful heart to the Immaculate Heart, the more I am filled with loathing for sin. What is ugly appears even uglier, what is wicked fully discloses its terrible perversity. Thus, in light of Mary, the sinner gains a deeper knowledge of his sins; his conscience becomes more keen and delicate. But in particular he experiences an increase in loathing and sorrow for sin, the more he places himself in the light of her loving, motherly heart. More and more he discovers how much sin betrays love and scorns and tramples underfoot the most tender heart of his mother. And this makes him more and more sorry. "O mother, forgive, and ask forgiveness of your son!"

At Fatima, Mary situates the sacrament of Penance in an even larger context: when making a confession we should think of *all* the offenses committed against her Immaculate Heart. Indeed, sin is never something individual, but affects the whole world. When one member suffers, then all the others suffer with it: through my sins I place myself on the side of a whole army of God's enemies, who shout "Crucify him", and strike his mother on the face. This thought throws into greater relief the value of Penance as a purification from such a terrible thing.

At Fatima, the sacrament of Penance is not only depicted as personal absolution from my sins; it acquires an additional value that encompasses the world. Through Penance in a spirit of reparation, my remorse extends to all offenses and thus becomes more perfect. For the most perfect sorrow for sin is that which considers the offended party and wants to make amends for everything that has ever been committed against him. In just this way I make amends not only for my share of the offenses committed against God. The thought of making reparation "consoles God and his mother" and makes amends for many sins. That is why Mary also promises the salvation of many souls, if we practice devotion to her Immaculate Heart.

Marriage and Family

Especially in matters of marriage and the family, the Immaculata is an example for spouses. The Holy Family of Nazareth is the model of the Christian family, yet it is the Immaculata who is especially the model of the wife and mother. Similarly, the relation between Mary and Joseph illuminates the sort of relationship that spouses should have.

Mary is the example of the wife and mother. How difficult it is for family members today to perform the duties of their state of life faithfully and to assume the precise place in the family community that Providence assigns to them! Pride and all the other sins make it especially difficult for the wife to maintain her seemingly subordinate role. And now the Immaculata stands before her, the Queen over all the angels and saints, the chosen mother of the Creator and Redeemer of the whole world. And what does she do? She leads the unassuming life of any housewife and mother of a family of low estate. Everything here is discretion, modesty, simplicity, great poverty, constant love of neighbor that hastens to help him in every need. When the other girls and women from the village meet her as she draws water from the well, they smile at her and go by without even suspecting that they have greeted the Mediatrix of All Graces, the co-Redemptrix and Queen of the universe. This humility and love of the hidden life is the special grace of the Immaculata for the family, without which a woman can never be a good mother and wife.

Mary was "espoused to a man whose name was Joseph" (*Mt.* 1:18, *Lk.* 1:27). This betrothal was the equivalent of marriage. Saint Thomas Aquinas says, along with the Church fathers, that a real marriage existed between Mary and Joseph, for "the form of matrimony consists in a certain inseparable union (*conjunctio*) of souls, by which husband and wife are pledged by a bond of mutual affection that cannot be sundered."[123] Thus there was an inseparable union of souls between

123. St. Thomas Aquinas, *Summa Theologica* III, q. 29, art. 2.

Mary and Joseph, the greatest of mutual love. Yet Mary belonged in an even greater measure entirely to God, devoted completely and utterly to God to the degree that God possesses her completely and utterly, and the Holy Ghost takes her to be his chosen sanctuary, his spouse. How can these two things be reconciled? We stand here at the origin of the mystery of love of neighbor; at the source of true community and friendship among souls; at the wellspring of true Christian marriage. Like Mary, every human being belongs in the first place to God completely and utterly. There is only one true love, which comes from God and returns to God, for God is love. The heart of Mary unceasingly lives her *fiat*; she trusts him completely and allows herself to be guided. Now the Holy Ghost wills that she give her heart to Saint Joseph, that her love for God be realized, so to speak, applied concretely, and allowed to shine forth and radiate in her devotion to Saint Joseph. Thus she takes back nothing of her total consecration to God; on the contrary, she lives it out fully by loving her husband completely with the love that she has for God. Thus Mary shows us an important rule of life: The more we love God and are devoted to him, the more we love our neighbor. And with that Mary gives us the key to a truly happy marriage, for a marriage is happy only when it is lived out in the atmosphere of true love. In order to build up a genuine communion of life, we must first have the genuine relation with God that Mary mediates for us, which has already been described in great detail. Through circumstances, actual graces, prompting of the Holy Ghost, through the working of secondary causes (parents, teachers, pastors, good reading, events, etc.), God shows us concretely what our way back to him is. This way is always an "application" of devotion to God in devotion to one's neighbor, since the great commandment of love always encompasses God and neighbor. The choice of a state of life is nothing other than a choice of how God wants this law of love to be applied. In the case of marriage, the stream of love that comes to us from the divine heart flows onward into the heart of the beloved neighbor, clear through him, so to speak, and back again to God. That means, concretely, that spouses love one another and are faithful to each other in the measure that they unite themselves with God and accordingly consecrate themselves totally to Mary. A happy marriage is not primarily a question of compatibility or mutual understanding, but rather a question of prayer and devotion to God.

In her love for Saint Joseph, Mary shows us that devotion to one's spouse and children unfolds and blossoms from devotion to God. And since the Immaculata is the Mediatrix of All Graces, the *forma Dei*, she is also the formative influence for the whole family. Problems in family life can all be traced to one cause: a lack of devotion. We are violent, rude, egotistical, stubborn, proud. We often want our own opinion to prevail and this gives rise to conflict, rebellion, disorder, lack of peace, confusion. Now Mary comes into the family like a ray of sunshine, like a fragrant breeze that creates a completely new atmosphere: she is total consecration and devotion and spreads this fragrance around. When a human being forgets himself and devotes himself, then peace and tranquility come into his heart. Pride and selfishness are noisy, while humility is quiet and peaceful. This atmosphere of peace, a gift from the Immaculata, is the best and sole basis for a happy marriage.

> The source of interior unease is always the same: self-love that flees from the cross.... The more a soul prays, the more peace and happiness it has. What does this look like concretely in everyday life? Such a soul

> does not live by its senses or by purely natural reason, but by faith.... The more it lives by faith, the more it lifts itself to the order that is infinitely higher than our natural life. It is guided by divine reason, by the will and the power of God. God knows what is best for the soul, and therefore it devotes itself entirely to God's will. That is why we strive to allow ourselves to be guided by the Immaculata and to desire only what she wants. If we live in this peace, then the City of the Immaculata will flourish mightily.[124]

We can say the same thing about any place where people live together, but especially in the family.

Marian Priesthood

The priest is the instrument that continues the mission of the Son and of the Holy Ghost in the world and in souls. But since these two missions occur only in and through Mary, the priesthood is connected with Mary in a special way. The priest will accomplish his vocation in the measure in which he gives Mary the same position in his life that she has for her divine priest-son. Now we have seen that Mary is the new Eve, the co-Redemptrix, the *alma socia* of Christ. Now, if she participates so intimately in his sacrifice, then she is likewise connected with his priesthood. He offers his sacrifice, and together with him she sacrifices herself and all that she has, namely her most beloved and precious treasure, Jesus himself. But because Christ is the High Priest for all eternity, Mary remains his associate for all eternity. Every priest on earth makes this sacrifice present through his participation in Jesus' priesthood. Therefore Mary is the associate of the eternal High Priest in every man who shares in his priesthood.

124. Saint Maximilian Kolbe, Conference dated March 3, 1938, KMK, p. 243.

Only if she is the "companion", the "spouse", the "associate", of our priesthood will it be fully and completely the priesthood of Christ.

Servant of Mary.

Mary and priests have the same task: offering Christ to the Father and giving him to mankind through the graces and gifts of the Holy Ghost. The priest continues Christ's objective work of redemption in space and time, but the essential condition for this work is Mary's act, which alone and for all time gave Christ to the world, in that she gave him a body, brought forth from her womb. Had she not pronounced her *fiat*, there would be no Christ, no priesthood, no sacrifice, no sacrament. She alone gave the world the one eternal High Priest, in whose priesthood all other priests only share and whose instruments they are. For this reason we must regard the priestly power of offering sacrifice and sanctifying as being dependent on the divine maternity. Christ's priests are only the unworthy servants of Mary in the sense that the cause of their priestly power, a power that was not given to Mary herself, finds its origin and cause in her *fiat*. As a consequence of this fact, we must regard the most important priestly function as being directly connected with and dependent on Mary's 'Yes': just as Mary, by her "Yes," infallibly drew down the Son of God to the world in her womb, so too the priest by the words of consecration infallibly brings Christ down to the world upon the altar.

Mary in the Priest's Mass.

The high point in the life of Christ and Mary is his "hour": the sacrifice on the cross. The high point of the priest's life is Holy Mass. Yet Christ accomplished his sacrifice on the cross in the most intimate union with the new Eve. The Holy Sacrifice of the Mass is the renewal of the sacrifice of Jesus Christ on the cross. For this reason the Immaculata, too, is present at every Holy Mass, just as she was present at the sacrifice on the cross. That means that the priest shares in Christ's loving devotion to Mary and likewise in Mary's loving compassion with her crucified son. As Mary assisted Christ, so she assists every priest. Christ willed to have need of her on Calvary, and likewise the priest has need of her at Holy Mass: indeed, Mary gives herself to the priest, so that the mystery of the sacrifice of the cross may be perfectly renewed. At Communion the priest again needs Mary, who obtains for him the grace to identify completely with Christ's sentiments. Here the prayer from the sequence, the *Stabat Mater,* acquires a profound meaning:

> "O sweet Mother! font of love,
> touch my spirit from above,
> make my heart with thine accord.
> Make me feel as thou hast felt;
> make my soul to glow and melt
> with the love of Christ, my Lord.
> Let me to my latest breath,
> in my body bear the death
> of that dying son of thine.
> Wounded with his every wound,
> steep my soul till it has swooned
> in his very blood away."

The priest's Mass is unthinkable without union with Mary; this is proved by the fact that Mary and Saint John stand beneath the cross. "Saint John was for her the continuation of Jesus Christ, and at this important moment of his ministry she belonged entirely to him: he was to enter into her way of thinking and allow his own

125. M. Olier, *La vie intérieure de la Très Sainte Vierge* (Paris, 1875), Chapter 16.

concerns to be absorbed by Mary's. He was given to her as her special priest, so that he might offer the sacrifice with the dispositions that were pleasing to her."[125] Saint John represents all believers, but especially the priest: every day when the priest carries out his most important office, he has the wonderful privilege of being accompanied invisibly by the Immaculata and of making present the great mystery of consolation and union which was accomplished on Calvary between the heart of Jesus and the heart of his mother and bride.

Mary in the Interior Life of the Priest.

This union of the priest with the mother in imitation of the union between Mary and John is continued in his interior life: what friendship, what pure love there was between Mary and John! There was something special and unique about it. The priest has been marked with the indelible character of Christ's priesthood, which gives him the power to make present and continue the work of the eternal High Priest. He is an *alter Christus*, and as such he should love Mary. He must love her as Christ loved her here on earth, and thereby he continues the union of Jesus and Mary through the ages. The Immaculate Heart of Mary complemented the heart of Jesus; similarly the heart of Mary complements the heart of the priest. He must not be alone; he needs her. And this is in accordance with the express will of Jesus: "Behold thy son—behold thy mother!"

> The love of Saint John for her was a purely spiritual love, without admixture of the senses, a love that found its source and nourishment in faith, yet a strong, intense, powerful, steadily burning love. This love brought him so vividly to Mary and united him so strongly and closely with her in Jesus that he saw her with the eyes of the spirit much more clearly at

> his side than if he were facing his own self. Finally, the trust that the one had in the other was so great, that their souls were united by an indissoluble bond for eternity; their union was so sure and firm that it appears that this trust and this union could not be purer or more godly in heaven itself.[126]

Mary in the Priestly Apostolate.

The priesthood consists in distributing God's graces (*dispensatores mysteriorum Dei*) to the world. "Because he has been placed between God and men, the priest must move God by his prayer and move men by his mercy and his compassion."[127] Stationed between heaven and earth, the priest is the mediator of God's graces. For this purpose the priest must become the father and mother of souls. In imitation of Christ, the priest develops the qualities of fatherhood, of being a director of souls. God has willed, however, that the priest should receive his maternal heart from Mary, who accompanies, assists, and consoles him in his priestly life and complements his priestly ministry, thus bringing it to perfection. She gives him her incomparable compassion for the weak and the suffering, the spirit of sacrifice which gives of itself without counting the cost. She teaches him a sense of tact and respect for the mystery of the human souls that are entrusted to his care.

Furthermore Mary is the Mediatrix of All Graces. Accordingly the priest cannot receive any graces for himself or bestow any grace on the faithful without her. This already begins with the grace of his priestly vocation and all the graces that have led him to the steps of the altar. As a priest he is a shepherd of souls. But this ministry remains completely barren without grace.

126. *Ibid.*

127. St. Thomas Aquinas, *In Epistula ad Hebreos*, Chapter 5, Lesson 1.

Every sinner who has converted through his pastoral ministry received these graces of conversion through Mary. Every soul that the priest has lifted from a lukewarm to a fervent state received these graces of sanctification from Mary. If the sun were to be suppressed, there would be no light or warmth or life on earth. If one were to suppress Mary's mediating activity, there would be no light or warmth or life in souls.

Although the priest absolutely needs Mary, she also needs the priest, for Christ wanted his Church to be a priestly Church, *i.e.,* his entire high-priestly work of mediating between God and mankind passes through the ministry of the priest. She expects his priests to commend souls to her, to communicate her greatness and glory to people, so that they can give themselves to her and she can in that way crush the devil's head in them. Therefore his ministry of mediation is, so to speak, twofold: making present the sole mediator, Jesus Christ, as his continuation, and being the mediator and connecting link of the bond between Mary and souls. Bossuet says[128] that, on the cross, Christ gave the virginal Apostle the three things that he considered the most valuable: he gave him his heart by allowing him to lean on his breast; he gave him his passion by calling him to be the only apostle beneath the cross, and he gave him his own mother to be his mother, so that "from that hour the disciple took her to his own". The heart of Jesus, the cross, and the Blessed Virgin: this is the threefold gift of eternal Love to its priests.

128. See Bossuet, *Panégyrique de saint Jean l'Evangéliste* (Paris, 1891), vol. 2, pp. 526-545.

Chapter Five

Christian Life in the Immaculata

Man's return to God consists in his acceptance of the redemptive work of Christ and of the sanctifying work of the Holy Ghost through the Immaculata. It is a life bearing the imprint of Mary's presence at every moment, in every walk of life, in every situation, in every expression of human existence (Chapters 2 and 3), imbued with the living waters of divine life, which flow to us through the channels of the sacraments and whose fruitfulness depends upon union with the Immaculata, who creates in us the best dispositions (Chapter 4). Nourished and strengthened by these divine mysteries, habits of goodness develop in us and our life becomes ever more pleasing to God; we are increasingly transformed into Christ. Our relation to God becomes more and more pure, deep, and perfect, which is expressed first in the fundamental attitude of truth toward God, that is, humility. Faith, hope, and charity unite us directly to God, while the other virtues enable us to fulfill God's will and finally to arrive at our destination. This entire Christian life, in turn, is made possible and realized through union with the

Immaculata. In this context it is simply not possible to present an outline of Church teaching on the virtues; we can only indicate how, at every step of the moral life, the mother of God is our example, helper, intercessor and, as it were, "mother of virtue": she brings forth virtue in us and gives life to it.

Foundation of the Christian life: Humility

"Pride transforms the virtues into sins. Humility transforms sins into virtues."[129] This lapidary statement of Saint Maximilian Kolbe shows us the importance of this virtue in our lives. In simple words the saint explains to his brothers the nature of humility:

> What comes from Satan is always characterized by a lack of humility. The soul marvels at its own weaknesses. That is a sign that it does not yet know itself. The saints did not marvel at their imperfections. If they marveled at anything, it was that they had not fallen lower. Humility is knowledge of oneself in accordance with the truth. The saints saw themselves as sinners and therefore they regarded the sufferings caused them by others as something they deserved. They trusted in God's mercy, not in themselves. Therefore we have no reason for discouragement. Otherwise it would be a sign that we were relying on ourselves, and then we are disappointed with ourselves. In the supernatural life we can do nothing without God's help. All effort and work in and of itself is a product of grace. Therefore we have no reason to be discouraged if we fall. If we fall often and deeper, then that is proof that we still have much self-love. Let us therefore use these falls for the purpose for which God allows them: to humble ourselves, so that we do not get excited but rather acknowledge our misery. If we were humble, then God would not

129. St. Maximilian Kolbe, Spiritual Exercises 1916, BMK, p. 358.

> allow a single sin. The Blessed Mother was humble her entire life. Nevertheless she recognized her dignity and likewise the great things that God accomplished in her. Humility does not consist in not recognizing the graces one has received, but rather in not attributing them to ourselves."[130]

This virtue is also the foundation of every fruitful apostolate.

> If we want to be sure of obtaining the greatest graces, we must strive to practice a profound humility and recognize that of ourselves we can do nothing.... Every good work comes from God, and it is his own gifts that he will crown in heaven. All that we are and have is from God; what we can do is possible for us through God.... Yet we owe all graces to the Mediatrix of All Graces. Therefore if we want to hasten the triumph of the Immaculate Heart throughout the world, if we want to bring it about as quickly as possible, then we must strive to let her guide all our efforts, and we must acknowledge that she must accomplish everything.[131]

But how are we to attain this great virtue? By following her own example, which we must accordingly keep ever in mind. Through her humility Mary was thoroughly pleasing to God. "He hath [graciously] regarded the humility of his handmaid, for behold from henceforth all generation shall call me blessed." Humility is the mother of the virtues, and the person in whom this mother-virtue was most perfectly present was chosen to become the mother of God. "He hath regarded the humility of his handmaid, which is to say that, in order to pour out upon her such a fullness of grace as the

130. Conference dated February 16, 1941, KMK, pp. 434-435.

131. Conference dated April 30, 1940, KMK, pp. 381-382.

Blessed Virgin received, God regarded nothing but the depth of her humility, through which she was able to receive the immense greatness of grace as though into the deepest recesses."[132] Through her humility Mary completely emptied herself, was so free of her own self that she could be completely and utterly attentive to God. This perfect knowledge of the truth about herself also enabled her to understand most profoundly God's condescension, whereby he humbled himself to dwell within her womb.

> Of all the weaknesses or of all the human insults which God in his goodness willed to suffer for us, the first, in the order of time, and almost the greatest, with respect to his condescension, was the fact that his infinite majesty deigned to be received in the womb of a woman and to be enclosed therein for nine months. For where did he empty himself to such an extent, or when did anyone ever see him so completely detached from himself? During that whole time this Wisdom spoke no word; to all outward appearances this might did nothing. This enclosed and hidden majesty makes himself known through no visible sign. On the cross God did not seem so weak; there, what appeared to be weak in him proved suddenly to be stronger than it is in all mankind: while dying he glorifies the good thief; while expiring, he inspires the centurion; one hour of pain during his passion awakens the compassion of the elements of creation, but also subjects the hostile powers to eternal pains. In his mother's womb, however, he who is there is as though he were not. And so omnipotence sleeps as though it were only powerlessness, and the eternal Word restrains itself in silence.[133]

132. Johannes a Sancte Thoma, *Cursus Theologicus*, vol. VIII, distinctio 19, articulus 6, n. 27.

133. St. Bernhard of Clairvaux, *In Annuntiatione dominica*, Sermo III, no. 4.

Mary's humility, therefore, is the perfect response (*re-actio*) to God's humility, and only by this response can a creature please God and return to him.

> O humility, through which the Woman became the mother of God, through which God came down from heaven to earth, through which souls have been brought from hell to heaven! This is the ladder that God gives you, the ladder with which you may climb from earth to heaven. By this ladder our fathers have climbed to heaven, and by it we must also climb up, for otherwise we shall never reach it.[134]

It is up to us now to imitate this example and to incorporate it into our lives. This happens by taking the following steps:

First we must humble ourselves before her, so that the graces that she wants to give us will not meet any resistance.

> "We are sinners; she is the Immaculata, without any sin whatsoever. How can we endure in her presence? We are not worthy to look at her statue, to pronounce her name, to think of her, for we are stained, but she is spotless. This is the most important point: to be clearly aware that we stand before her as sinners who have been soiled. Only then can we ask her for grace, of which we are completely unworthy, to be able to think of her and to meditate on her glories."[135]

We begin to become humble when our prayer is humble.

Then we must enter into Mary's interior life and, like a little child, strive to imitate her. And since the mystery of humility is most gloriously resplendent at the moment of the angel's announcement, we have to imitate this precise attitude of Mary. What is taking place in Mary at this decisive hour? First she meditates on God and his

134. St. Bernhard of Clairvaux, *Tractatus de statu virtutum*, Prima Pars, ch. 13.
135. Conference dated September 26, 1937, KMK, p. 171.

infinite majesty. he is the unqualified Lord of all. Then she looks at herself, to the very depths of her being. Although she is blessed among all creatures, chosen for the most exalted dignity that can ever be given to a human being, she knows profoundly that all this is a gift from God, who has regarded the worthlessness of his slave girl in mercy, for despite her exalted vocation she is nothing in and of herself, brought out of nothingness, and having nothing of her own. And from this meditation on this twofold abyss—the abyss of God's majesty and the abyss of her own nothingness—she draws the logical conclusion: "Thou art everything; I am nothing. Thou art everything in me. Let it be done to me according to thy word. Behold thy handmaid!" We know what an ocean of divine love this total consecration set into motion for the sake of the lost world. Three times a day we recall this mystery in the *Angelus*. The number three is the number of totality, completion, perfection, constancy, and endlessness: unceasingly during the day we should imitate in our lives this attitude of Mary. Whatever comes our way in the course of the day is like God's call through the angel to do his will here and now. With Mary we meditate on God's greatness and our own nothingness and repeat with her again and again: *Fiat! Ecce! Magnificat!* That is training in humility.

The struggle for humility is a battle; we can even say that it is the greatest, most difficult, most violent of battles. If Mary is humility in person, then she is opposed by pride in person, in Satan. When Saint Maximilian regards man's return to God as nothing less than enlistment in the army of the Immaculata in order to fight against the foe, it is simply because he knows that Lucifer's pride is totalitarian and that only the humble handmaid can withstand it and will ultimately crush his head. It is important, therefore, when using military terminology, to realize that the essential element in the whole campaign is a renunciation of pride, renewed many times each day, and an assent to the truth, which is humility—and doing this solely under the protective mantle of the Immaculata.

Finally we must know that this battle will never end, as long as we live on earth. It is said that self-love dies only a quarter of an hour after our death. It is so overpowering that it clings to everything, even to the holiest things. Someone does penance, prays well, strives for sanctity, for perfection, and then turns around and says, "Oh, I know all that already!" Yes, self-love is everywhere. The soul can tell how much we are affected by it when humiliations come. Then we can be sure as to whether we are really humble.... But in this respect, too, we are capable of everything through the Immaculata. There is no pride so great that it cannot be uprooted from us with her help. The very fact that the soul turns to the Immaculata is already humility.

Prayer Life

In what way does the Immaculata make our prayer life productive? Prayer is lifting up the soul to God in order to adore him, thank him, present petitions to him, and ask his forgiveness. No one on earth accomplished this so perfectly as Mary did. As with everything else, so too Mary's prayer becomes the "form", the prototype and example for our prayer, *i.e.,* our relationship with God.

Union with God.

The purpose of prayer is contact with God, union with God. The Immaculata leads us again and again back to the essentials when we, in our superficiality, forget or neglect the real meaning of prayer. And what is the essential thing? Living in solitude as a twosome, being "alone with the Solitary One". Blessed Elizabeth of the Holy Trinity was able to comprehend the prayer life of the Immaculata in an especially profound way: "What must have gone on in the Blessed Virgin's soul when she possessed within herself the Word-made-flesh, the gift of God after the Incarnation? With what silence, recollection and adoration did she bury herself in the depths of her soul so as to embrace this God, whose mother she had become?"[136] Her whole life was unceasing, silent adoration of the divine Word, completely immersed in the loving life of the most Holy Trinity.

> 'She kept all these words and pondered them in her heart.' That is the best definition of meditation, of contemplative prayer. It seems to me that the conduct of the Blessed Virgin during the months between the Annunciation by the angel and the birth of Jesus is the model for all interior souls. With what peace and recollection Mary got up and set about doing everything. All things, even the most commonplace, were divinized in her, for through it all she kept adoring the gift of God. But this did not keep her from devoting herself to external things when necessary, from practicing love of neighbor. The Gospel tells us that Mary 'went into the hill country in haste into a city of Juda, and she entered into the house of Zachary and saluted Elizabeth'. her external love of neighbor never diminished the ineffable vision that she contemplated.[137]
>
> There is one creature that was the honor of the glory of the most Holy Trinity. She responded fully to the divine election about which the Apostle speaks: she was always pure, spotless, flawless, in the eyes of the Thrice-Holy God. Her soul is so simple, the

136. Bl. Elisabeth de la Trinité, *Letter to her Sister*, November 1903, in P. Philipon, *La doctrine spirituelle de Soeur Elisabeth de la Trinité* (Bruges, 1938), p. 184.

137. *Ibid.*, p. 187.

movements of her soul are so profound, that no one can reach her. She seems to reproduce on earth the life of the divine Being, of simple Being. She is so transparent, so light, that one could mistake her for light itself. Yet she is only the mirror of the Sun of Justice, *speculum justitiae*. 'The Virgin kept all these things in her heart.' Her whole story can be summed up in these few words: she lived in her heart, so deeply that our sight can no longer follow it. When I read in the Gospel that Mary hastened to the hill country of Juda in order to perform her charitable service to her cousin Elizabeth, then I see her passing by, so beautiful, so peaceful, so majestic, so interiorly recollected with the divine Word. As in his case, so with her also, it was always the same prayer: *Ecce*—Behold, I am.... What? The handmaid of the Lord, the least of all creatures. And she, his mother, said that.[138]

Therefore our prayer, too, must resemble this, even though it may assume various forms according to the mood, the character, and the state of life of the person praying, as well as the circumstances and various types of prayer. We can say that prayer is always defined by two fundamental lines: love of God and love of neighbor. Sometimes the goal is God himself, to meditate on God alone, to glorify, console, or love him, to ask him for forgiveness and to make ourselves little in his presence, to allow ourselves to be led, taught, and loved by him. It consists of drinking from the spring, an anticipation of the eternal homecoming, leaving time so as to "live a bit of eternity". "O my God, O Trinity whom I adore, help me to forget myself completely so as to dwell in you, motionless and peaceful, as though my soul were already abiding in eternity. Nothing should be able to

138. Ibid. p. 191.

disturb my peace or draw me away from you, O my Unchanging Lord; instead every minute should lead me further into the depths of your mystery!"[139] Saint Louis Marie de Montfort compares Mary to a magnificent mountain on which God has taken up his dwelling place, "on which Jesus teaches and dwells forever, where one is transfigured with him, where one dies with him, where one ascends with him into heaven."[140] Therefore, we must unite ourselves with Mary in prayer, and that means climbing this mountain, our ascent to God. The same saint calls Mary the oratory, the house in which God dwells, the place in which we find him. Only in this house is there the right atmosphere: most profound recollection, reverent silence, ineffable beauty, and simplicity, the incense of adoration, the atmosphere of God's presence, heaven on earth!

Apostolic Prayer

The other purpose of prayer is apostolic, turning to God in order to save souls, one's own first, then the souls of those entrusted to us, and finally all souls. Praying this prayer confirms the conviction that the conversion and sanctification of souls is a work of grace and thus that everything depends on God alone, whereas we, for all our activity, are only God's "worthless instruments", which he employs out of condescension. The apostolic purpose, however, is also an important incentive for us, since we are often very negligent in our prayers. Knowing that the eternal salvation of many people, perhaps of my dearest friends, can depend on my prayer, forces me, so to speak, to get down on my knees. For this reason Saint Maximilian describes apostolic prayer as one of the most important weapons of the knight of the

139. *Ibid.*, p. 349.
140. Seraphic Prayer, LGM, p. 685.

Immaculata.[141] In his conferences for the brothers in the City of the Immaculata he mentions almost every day this foundation of all apostolic work. At the moment when they were setting their highest records, when the number of brothers surpassed seven hundred and millions of copies of the magazine *Knight of the Immaculata* were being published, when externally they were having their greatest successes, the saint lamented:

> We think too little about the Immaculata. We read too little about her, we draw near to her too infrequently. Everyone should examine himself: how often each day have I turned to her? He will have to be ashamed. We have not been childlike enough for her to govern us so that all our actions might belong to her and she might be our Queen.[142] Why was our zeal for the Immaculata in souls not yet what it could be? . . . We can honestly admit that we have turned much too infrequently to the Immaculata. How far we still are from the sort of life in which she rules in us completely, and there is no longer even the smallest space in our soul that does not belong to the Immaculata! For that we need prayer, honest prayer, and again prayer, so as to know her and love her as she must be loved.[143] We read in the Old Testament that Moses prayed with hands upraised for the Israelites as they were battling with the enemy. Whenever he allowed his hands to sink, the Israelites would begin to lose. So we too must have our hands raised in prayer; essentially the whole future depends on it.... Let us examine our consciences, whether we truly appreciate the value of prayer, and what we are doing in order to make up for this deficiency.[144]

141. See Fr. Karl Stehlin, *The Immaculata our Ideal* (Angelus Publishing, 2006?) pp. GT110-114.

142. Conference dated November 6, 1938, KMK, p. 304.

143. KMK, p. 302.

144. KMK, pp. 372-373.

Prayer in Light of the Apparitions at Fatima

The apparitions at Fatima, too, assure us of the importance of prayer. It is very significant that the angel who, in the second apparition surprised the children while they were playing by the well, called to them as follows: "What are you doing there? Pray! Pray much! The Sacred Hearts of Jesus and Mary are full of mercy and inclined to you. Offer prayers and sacrifices unceasingly to the Most-High!" Just as she did a few decades before in Lourdes, so too here the Immaculata guides the children into the spirit of prayer. Not only in the sense that the children learned several prayers firsthand (the Angel's prayer, "O my Jesus..." and various ejaculations), and not just the demand that they pray much, especially the daily rosary. Through the supernatural light that Mary communicated to them during the first three apparitions, the children were privileged to experience the whole depth of the life of prayer. Yet the children did not go for their own sakes to this school of the Immaculate Heart; we, too, can and must profit from it. Mary knows how difficult it is for us these days really to pray, and therefore she holds up the simple prayer of little children as an example that we can imitate, so as to be united with God in the shortest possible time. That is also one aspect of the promises made by the mother of God at Fatima. And what does the prayer of the children of Fatima consist of? When we look at the spiritual profile of Francesco and Jacinta, we see the guidelines of prayer that have been described above carried out in a perfect but easily accessible way.

Francesco contemplated God and how he was offended by mankind. And so, after the first apparition of the mother of God, he said, "I loved seeing the angel

The Pilgrim Statue *Our Lady of Fatima, Queen of Peace*, owned by the Padre Pio Institute, Ottawa, Canada. It is not only one of the most beautiful Fatima statues in the world, but many graces have been given throughout the many pilgrimages all over the world, particularly in 2005 in Eastern Europe, where in Ukraine many people converted to the Catholic Faith.

very much and our Lady even more. But what I loved the most was seeing our Lord in that light that the Blessed Mother put into our hearts. I love God so much! But he is so sad because there are so many sins. We must never commit another one."[145] After the apparition on July 13 we hear him say the following momentous words: "What is God like? No one can explain that. Really, nobody will ever be able to say. But it hurts so much that he is so sad! Oh, if only I could console him!"[146] And from then on that would be his whole life, especially his prayer: "I love to pray alone, so as to think about Jesus and console him, for he is so sad!"[147] Isn't the Immaculata teaching us through him the most profound manner of loving prayer, namely her own? Indeed, in her boundless compassion under the cross she did precisely that: console her son. So we too must find a few moments in which to be alone with Christ and to be there for him exclusively and thereby to console him, by the simple fact that we stand with her under the cross. Although contemporary man no longer has time for God, who created him; although he is so indifferent that he finds it boring to watch an hour with Christ, we at least should show our love for him by having a little time for him and by trying to console him with our loving presence and our compassion. But what is the result of such an attitude? This, too, is demonstrated by the example of little Francesco: in a very short time his love for God reached perfection, and a few months later he was already allowed to serve the Immaculata forever in heaven.

Through Jacinta, Mary leads us into the depths of apostolic prayer. All prayer for souls is first and foremost a prayer that they will be saved from the eternal damna-

145. SFL, p. 133.
146. SFL, p. 137.
147. SFL, p. 146.

tion that we have all merited by our sins. Sister Lucia writes about her cousin: "The vision of hell had horrified her so much that all penances and mortifications seemed to her insufficient to keep some souls from going to hell." The young visionary shows what a little child can do for the salvation of souls through many ejaculatory prayers and sacrifices. In this same vein Cardinal Cerejera of Lisbon is said to have remarked that she snatched more souls from hell through her prayers and sacrifices during her short life than thousands of missionaries during their whole life times. We observe a similar ardent love for souls especially in the patroness of the missions, Saint Thérèse of the Child Jesus, and in the Carmelite spirituality in general.

Therefore, at Fatima, the Immaculate Heart of Mary wants to tell us that we should immerse ourselves in prayer without fear. If little, uneducated children can be guided by her in a short time to union with God, she can accomplish the same in our souls as well.

Living in Faith, Hope, and Charity

The supernatural organism that has been bestowed on us in the sacrament of Baptism must now grow through the practice of the theological virtues. Here Mary appears as the mother who nourishes and raises her children, causing them to grow "in age, wisdom and grace before God and men".

Faith

According to the Council of Trent, faith is "the beginning, the foundation, and the root of all justification." However, a firm faith is demanded above all in times when the truth is being fought, weakened and obscured. "Lord, increase my faith, help my unbelief": this life of faith is renewed in us by the Immaculata.

First of all, belief in Mary's glories is an intense exercise of the virtue of faith. One can marvel at Christ without faith, and many people in fact do just that: they regard him as a leader, an example, a reformer, a philosopher, or even a friend of all men; a heroic figure who had great influence on all mankind. Mary, however, cannot be understood in a merely natural light. Viewed in that way, she would be nothing but an unassuming, poor woman who says almost nothing and also does almost nothing. Mary makes no sense to unbelievers. She is what she is solely in the supernatural order, and only in the light of faith can she be recognized. If you see a scholar or an artist in a great church during a solemn ceremony, you can't tell yet what brought him there: faith or some purely human motive (aesthetic sense, the desire to be seen, ties of family, or friendship, etc.). But if you see the same individual kneeling before a statue of the Blessed Mother and praying the rosary, then you know that you are dealing with a believer.

Although Christ himself is our greatest example for all the other virtues, this is not the case with faith and hope, since Christ always possessed the beatific vision and could never lose it. Faith, however, is conviction about the invisible revelation of God, to which I adhere on the basis of his authority. Accordingly, the real and noblest example of faith is Mary: "Blessed art thou that hast believed!" She had to believe in the angel's words, that she would become the mother of God without losing her virginity. She had to believe that the small, weak child that she bore in the stable and laid in the manger was not only the Messiah but God himself. She had to believe in his everlasting triumph even at the moment when he was hanging on the cross and apparently had suffered the ultimate defeat. How many times

God demanded of her a heroic act of faith! And just as many times she responded without hesitating even an instant. Mary hands this faith on to all those who entrust and consecrate themselves to her.

Isn't meditation on the great mysteries of our faith through Mary in the Holy rosary precisely the means which preserves souls from ruin? At Lourdes and Fatima Mary requested the daily recitation of the rosary firstly so as to preserve in us the true Faith. Sister Lucia of Fatima often underscores this in her letters. To her priest-nephew she writes, "We must pray the rosary every day. That is the prayer that the Blessed Mother recommended to us the most, as though to give us an effective shield in these days of demonic attack. The devil knows that we are saved through prayer. Therefore he wages such a battle against it, so as to ruin us."[148] She leads a veritable crusade against the modernistic post-conciliar campaign against the rosary:

> Why should this prayer, which God has taught us and so often recommended to us, be outdated today? It is easy to discern here the deceit of the devil and his accomplices, who try to distance souls from God by preventing them from praying. Don't let yourself be deceived. Enlighten the souls that have been entrusted to you and pray the rosary with them every day.[149]
>
> The decline in the world is without a doubt the result of the lack of the spirit of prayer. It was precisely by way of anticipating this error that the Blessed Virgin so emphatically requested that we pray the rosary. And the rosary is, after the Holy Liturgy, the most suitable prayer of all for maintaining faith in souls; that is why the devil has unleashed such a campaign against it. The rosary is the strongest weapon

148. Fr. S. Martins dos Reis, *Uma Vida ao servico de Fatima* (Porto, 1973), p. 380.
149. *Ibid.*

that can defend us on the battlefield.[150]

In his Marian encyclical, Pope Leo XIII mentions again and again the connection between the rosary and the Faith.

> The contemplation of these august mysteries, contemplated in their order, affords to faithful souls a wonderful confirmation of faith, protection against the disease of error, and increase of the strength of the soul. The soul and memory of him who thus prays, enlightened by faith, are drawn towards these mysteries by the sweetest devotion, are absorbed therein and are surprised before the work of the Redemption of mankind, achieved at such a price and by events so great.[151]

"Therefore it is no exaggeration to declare that in places, peoples, and families where the rosary is honored and diligently prayed, there is no need to fear the loss of faith through ignorance and serious errors."[152]

Hope

Hope causes us to yearn for the supernatural truth acknowledged in faith and to trust in God's promises. It is the virtue that makes us aspire to God with boundless trust in his gracious help. Now every fiber of Mary's being is yearning for God and boundless trust in him; that is why the Church calls her the "Mother of holy hope" and even "our hope". There was even one moment in which we can say that Mary alone preserved hope: on Holy Saturday, when Christ lay in the tomb and everything seemed to be in vain and even those who were most loyal in the faith in Christ doubted

150. Letter from Sr. Lucia to Fr. Umberto Maria Pasquale dated November 26, 1970, cited in: Br. Michel de la Trinité, *Toute la vérité sur Fatima*, vol. III (Saint-Parres-les-Vaudes, 1985), p. 512.
151. Leo XIII., Encyclical *Octobri Mense*, GWP, p. 50.
152. Leo XIII., Encyclical *Magnae Dei Matris*, GWP, p. 64.

because of his horrible death, Mary preserved this hope, without seeing how it could be fulfilled. This is hope in its purest form, namely a reliance on God without any human assurances, solely based upon his word, in which one places unconditional trust. Therefore, Mary herself was so filled to overflowing with the purest, unspotted hope that, as co-Redemptrix, she can bring forth this grace in all her children. She is thus fittingly called the Mother of Holy Hope, and the Church applies to her the saying of eternal Wisdom: ". . .in me is all hope of life and of virtue" (*Ecclu.* 24:15). That means that this virtue takes form in Mary. When I say, "I hope in God," then at the same time I likewise say, "Mary, my hope!" In fact the certainty and the confidence that I will remain true to God to the end is not of my own doing, but is rather an unmerited grace which comes to me, as all graces do, through the Immaculata. Thus Saint Bernard says that Mary is the comprehensive cause, the whole reason-for-being of my hope. And Saint Peter Damian is even more explicit: that she is capable of raising those in despair to hope in eternal happiness.[153] That means that both of the basic attitudes of faith have their firm foundation and their highest expression in Mary: on the one hand, Mary awakens in me a yearning for God and for true goods; on the other hand, Mary is the fulfillment of God's promises.

Hope as a yearning for God turns a human being away from the false "hopes" in worldly goods and toward the genuine, eternal goods that alone can slake his thirst and satisfy his hunger. In this sense hope is actually the virtue of conversion, which means precisely "turning away from worldly goods and turning to God". When faith shows us the glory of eternal happiness, the

153. Dom B. Marechaux, *Notre Dame de la Sainte Espérance, convertissez nous* (Mesnil-Saint-Loup, 1961), p. 11.

yearning to possess these goods grows in our hearts. And the more this yearning grows, the more peaceful the soul becomes, the less it is tormented by the desires and wishes of the world, which formerly plunged it into such great unrest. Saint Augustine says that the soul that is created for God remains restless until it has found its rest in God, just as the needle of a compass is restless until it points exactly toward the magnetic pole. But as soon as the soul is correctly oriented, it finds peace. All the graces of conversion that Mary sends to us can be summarized as an ever greater reliance on holy hope. Père Emmanuel had a profound grasp of this spiritual reality and promoted devotion to "our Lady of Holy Hope" in his parish. As his parishioners formed the habit of saying the short prayer, our Lady of Holy Hope, convert us!" his parish underwent an extraordinary transformation and became one of the most exemplary parishes in the whole world.

Hope, however, is also self-abandonment to God's promises. If Mary is called "our hope", then her presence is the guarantee that these promises will also be fulfilled, indeed, that they have already begun to be fulfilled in her. She was in fact the hope of our first parents, when they received the great promise about the Woman who would crush the serpent's head. Since then she has been the hope of the human race. Isaiah connects the promise of the Messiah with the miracle of the virgin birth. But especially after Christ's Ascension, Mary remains the hope of Christians.

> God gave us Mary to be our hope. After all, it is his business how he prefers to answer our prayers. Whoever calls on Mary invokes his dearest creature, touches the most tender spot in his heart—and therefore finds that his prayer is answered. Catholic Christianity has known this for a long time....

Trouble teaches us to pray, and trouble is what really teaches us to prize the loyalty and help of a friend. In every age there has been great trouble among the Christian people, and out of this trouble has grown trust in Mary. And because it has never been disappointed, no one can uproot it again from the heart of the Christian people."[154]

Probably no one has more clearly expressed this hope that is personified in Mary than Saint Bernard in his prayer: "Remember, O most gracious Virgin Mary, that never was it known that anyone who fled to thy protection, implored thy help, or sought thine intercession was left unaided. Inspired with this confidence, I fly unto thee...."

CHARITY

Mary as the Mediatrix of All Graces gives us a share also in the most profound mystery of her heart: "I am the Mother of Fair Love." Her Immaculate Heart is nothing less than the purest love for God and souls, the purest imitation of the heart of Jesus.[155] Love is union. The hearts that love each other become one: their thoughts and desires, words and deeds, and finally a union of their whole lives. Now Mary, as the Mother and Queen of Love, receives this grace of uniting men with God and with one another; her heart is the magnet that draws everyone to herself and arranges everything for the best. Through her most intimate union with the Holy Ghost, she has the privilege of being the heart and soul of the Church, which enlivens all the members of the Mystical Body and causes them to work together in harmony in that great spiritual organism. And she does that by giving each one a share in her love. As she formerly showered

154. Josef Dillersberger, *Die Stimme deines Grusses* (Salzburg, 1936), pp. 66-67.
155. See above, Ch. 3.2 on the Mediatrix of all graces.

all her maternal love on the "blessed fruit of her womb", and devoted herself with extraordinary tenderness and care to the Child Jesus, so now she surrounds his Mystical Body, the Church, with the same motherly care and motherly love.

The *Acts of the Apostles* speak quite explicitly about the great love that united the first Christians with one another. They "had but one heart and one soul" (*Acts* 4:32). And the pagans were compelled to testify about them: "See how they love one another." But what is reason why this love was so great and outstanding then?

> The first congregation of Christians in Jerusalem flourished so much in charity because they sheltered in their midst the most loving woman who ever walked on earth—this mother, who embraced the whole community with a magnificent and boundless maternal love as though it were her very own son.... This love was truly the kind of love that is supposed to be, as Paul has described for us: 'Charity is patient, is kind; charity envieth not ... is not puffed up.... Charity never falleth away' (*1 Cor.* 13:4, 8). Everyone admits that Paul is sketching here an ideal picture of love. Only the charity that filled Mary's heart and poured out from her heart upon the early Church—only that charity lived up to the ideal. This pure image of love originates in her heart! She gave it to the Church at the beginning to accompany her on her earthly journey—who could ever thank her enough for that?[156]

Love as reparation. What is the supreme expression of love for us, for fallen, sinful mankind? Reparation. The sacrifice of Jesus Christ on the cross is the supreme act of charity. And this loving act is an act of atonement and reparation for the injustice that had been

156. Josef Dillersberger, *Das neue Wort über Maria* (Salzburg, 1947), pp. 183-192.

committed. Charity with respect to sin and the sinner is expressed in atonement: for someone who loves and has the misfortune of having offended, the beloved can continue to speak about love only if this injustice has been atoned for and the obstacle to love has been removed. This is precisely the central message of Fatima. Already during the apparition of the angel, this theme was expressly mentioned: first the angel asks the children to pray in reparation, and in the second apparition, he asks them to make sacrifices, and in the third, he introduces them to the greatest act of atonement, the only one worthy of God: the Eucharistic Sacrifice. The Angel's Prayer is a prayer of reparation for our "offenses, sacrileges and indifference". During the third apparition, as the children were receiving the mystical Communion, the angel said directly: "Eat the body and drink the blood of Jesus Christ, who is terribly offended by ungrateful men. Atone for their crimes and console your God." On June 13, 1917, Mary showed the children her heart, which was unceasingly pierced by thorns. "We understood that this was the Immaculate Heart of Mary, which was offended by the sins of mankind and demanded reparation."[157] The result of this vision for the three children was an intimate knowledge and a deep love for the Immaculate Heart of Mary. "From that day on we felt in our hearts a much more ardent love for the Immaculate Heart of Mary." And how did the children express this love? Precisely in acts of atonement and reparation. This was in fact the great purpose of Fatima, as confirmed by Mary's apparition in Pontevedra, in which Mary communicated the essence of devotion to her Immaculate Heart. Indeed, reparation is the "pattern" and the intention that permeates and defines all the related practices

157. SLF., p. 171.

(Communion, Confession, rosary, meditation). The postulant Lucia again saw Mary's heart pierced by thorns and heard these moving words: "See, my daughter, my heart surrounded by thorns, which ungrateful men inflict upon me at every moment by their blasphemies and ingratitude, while there is no one to make reparation for them and thereby to draw them out of my heart.... You, at least, strive to console me...."[158] Love wants to make reparation for the evil that is committed against Mary. Reparation is the annihilation of the wrong that has been done, the restoration of wholeness, the healing of the injured heart.

But this reparation is not only an act of heroic and pure love for God and the Immaculata; it is also the summit of true love of neighbor. The latter consists of wishing our neighbor what is best, loving him as Christ loved him, and consequently desiring his happiness, his salvation, and doing everything possible so that he attains this salvation. But what is the most important thing we should do, when we reflect that we are all sinners? The supreme act of love of neighbor is reparation for the sins of the neighbor and the request that God might let his mercy shine upon him. Christ himself explained this purpose of the devotion to Sr. Lucia: "My daughter, the reason why the Immaculate Heart of Mary inspired Me to request this little act of reparation was to stir up my mercy with regard to this reparation, so as to forgive souls that have had the misfortune of offending it. But you, through your prayers and sacrifices, seek unceasingly to fan the flames of my mercy for these poor souls."[159] In Fatima, in our time, when "charity grows cold" in many people, God once again fans the flames of the love that is most fitting for us poor sinners and also

158. SLF, p. 207.
159. Fr. Antonio Maria Martins, S.J., *Fatima, Documentos* (Porto, 1976), p. 409.

has the most profound consequences: reparation! And just as a son can sooner tolerate being insulted himself than listening to someone revile his beloved mother, so Christ is infinitely pleased with reparation for the sins that are committed against his most Blessed Mother. And if our love for Mary is enkindled in this way, then Mary can united herself completely with us and lead us to the summit of love for God and neighbor.

Let us not forget, however, that the word "love" is often misused, especially nowadays. "What does love consist of? Emotions? No, emotion is not the essential thing. Emotion is passing; it is here today and gone tomorrow.... Perfect love is perfect obedience to the Immaculata."[160] "He that hath my commandments and keepeth them, he it is that loveth Me" (Jn 14:21). And since there is no greater love than the one that lays down its life for its friends, the realization and actualization of true love consists of obedience and sacrifice.

Obedience

Mary is the prototype of obedience. The essence of sanctity is conforming our will to the will of God. Now the inmost essence of Mary's infinite purity and spotlessness consists of the fact that from the first moment of her conception she was entirely subject to this will, without any shadow, without any hesitation, without even the least resistance.

Obedience in itself does not mean a lack of freedom, much less an absence of personal initiative. Only when perfect conformity to God's will is lacking can a creature experience obedience to God as something contrary to "freedom and personal initiative", because his initiative is perverted by sin and has become destructive. Then he feels that conformity to God's will is a limit imposed on

160. St. Maximilian Kolbe, Conference dated May 7, 1938, KMK, pp. 271-272.

his self-affirmation and lack of restraint, which is in reality the opposite of freedom, namely an enslavement of the will to mindless instinct or dead matter. Conformity to God's will, however, cannot be a consequence of choice and personal initiative but necessarily precedes that choice. For the will of God is something already given as the one goal of man, which he can only affirm if he follows his reason and wants to attain fulfillment, happiness. This conformity to God's will, therefore, is the measure of the holiness and perfection of every created person and the motive and purpose for every choice and initiative.

The Immaculata is the model of obedience. If this conformity is accomplished without qualification and furthermore is accomplished from the very first moment of a person's existence—in other words, if from the first moment of conception not even the least stain of sin mars this conformity to God's will, then this person possesses the greatest possible sanctity and God gives himself entirely to this person: Mary is, from the beginning of her existence, "full of grace". Now if God at a particular moment calls her and announces his will to her and she freely consents to this will, then she performs the act that is most pleasing to God. By her 'Yes' she fulfill the whole ultimate purpose of created things: to be the praise of God's glory, to please God without end. From the creature's perspective, this aptitude of the will for perfect obedience, for immaculate, total, and pure conformity to God's will, is the source of the heart's yearning for infinite love, a yearning that is boundlessly fulfilled in the Immaculata.

Thus we see how the Immaculata forms in us the spirit of obedience: she directs our sights to God and makes us understand that God's reality and God's will are one and the same. If we receive God's truth, then we simultaneously recognize his holy will. She brings to our mind the destination that we profess. But then she influences our souls, so that we conform ourselves to this will of God. She demonstrates this practical conformity in her own life, namely her subjection to the will of those through whom God has revealed his will to us. But she also manifests the limitations of these instruments: she obeys the high priests and scribes in a different way, and in yet another way she obeys Saint Joseph. She is aware of the limitations of human instruments, and by keeping God constantly in view, the supreme and ultimate object of her obedience, she is able to understand precisely the role of God's instruments.

But it is always difficult for us to be obedient, since we live in a very rebellious age, which proclaims the independence of man from any and all authority; because of this, God lightens for us the burden of obedience by presenting it to us as the will of the Immaculata.

> You can unhesitatingly use an expression like, 'I desire to fulfill the Immaculate's will,' . . . because she wills what Jesus wills, whereas Jesus wills what his Father wills. Thus her will differs in no way from that of her son and the Father. Indeed, by yielding yourself unreservedly to her you will by this very fact not only show that you love the will of God, but also proclaim the truth that her will is so perfect that it deviates in nothing from the will of God; thus you will give glory to God the Father and the Son for creating a creature as perfect as she is and for having made her his own mother.[161]

How hard it is for a man to stand in front of an unadorned law which he must carry out, against his own wishes. How easy it becomes for him to carry out this

161. Fragments of a book on the Immaculata, KR, 196.

law, however, when he recognizes that it is the will of someone whom he loves very much.

Supernatural Obedience.

We owe it to the Immaculata likewise that this obedience is also an act that pleases God and produces supernatural fruit. We would like to love the Immaculata more and more. But how? Through supernatural obedience: "Perfect obedience is the perfecting of love for the Immaculata. If we accomplish our task with the same contentment, despite repugnance to our senses or a complete lack of emotion, then our obedience is perfect and supernatural.... The more we walk along this way of supernatural obedience, the more the Immaculata can guide us."[162] If a soldier were to ask, during a war, what he should do in order to accomplish the most for his fatherland, they would tell him that he should heed his superiors as conscientiously as possible. If they give the order to fight, then he should fight; to march, then he should march; if quickly, then quickly; if they order him to retreat, he should retreat. In contrast, what sort of a soldier would it be who did not always know his commander's plans and began to do whatever he wanted, shooting when he was supposed to be quiet, advancing when they were supposed to retreat. That would be the end of discipline. And here we must add that in this case the superior can make a mistake. God's will, in contrast, is infinite and infallible. Therefore a person can do the most for the cause of the Immaculata if he or she fulfills the will of God perfectly, as perfectly as possible. Moreover, someone who perfectly fulfills God's will can boldly say that he is doing so much that even God, who is Almighty and infinite, could do no more in his place. Therefore someone who perfectly

162. Conference dated May 7, 1938, KMK, pp. 271-272.

fulfills God's will does infinite good for souls. And that is the most perfect way, for Jesus Christ himself has showed us this way. If there were a more perfect one, he would surely have chosen it. Yet he was obedient to the Blessed Mother and Saint Joseph for thirty years and said that in this way he "always did the Father's will".[163]

Suffering and Sacrifice

Through suffering and his sacrifice on the cross, Christ redeemed the world. Accordingly, to imitate Christ perfectly, we must be "soldiers of Jesus' cross", friends of the cross, as Saint Louis Marie de Montfort says. Now this is very, very difficult. For this reason the Lord gives us here, too, his mother as an example, but also as a compassionate mother, who helps her child to walk this way of the cross. In her the yoke becomes easy and the burden light.

The Mother of Sorrows

Perhaps the most frightening thing about human suffering is helplessness. When we are forced to witness the suffering of a beloved person, without being able to do something for him, this causes stabbing pain. If a cross comes into our own life and we are powerless to do anything about it, this helplessness causes the worst pain. This helplessness demands a response: One may oppose it and protest against the suffering—and when it is unavoidable, one becomes sarcastic, embittered, rebellious, and desperate. Or else one resigns oneself, abandons oneself to fate, becomes indifferent to everything, just sits and vegetates (which is another form of despair). A temporary solution is the attempt to put off the unavoidable, to divert one's attention, to deceive oneself as long as possible—which is especially easy today, when

163. Conference dated April 18, 1937, KMK, pp. 116-117.

the world has countless distractions of this sort ready to go. All these sorts of reactions end terribly: after a life in which one wastes one's time in running away from the cross and thus never does anything really valuable, one finally succumbs to it like a trapped beast. But who gives us the strength not to give in to this urge of our fallen nature and to walk instead the opposite way, accepting the cross and suffering? Of course, the example of our Redeemer, who has revealed to us the value of suffering as the greatest form of love. Yet our Lord's way of suffering infinitely surpasses our abilities: "Whither I go, thou canst not follow me now; but thou shalt follow hereafter." Therefore in order to walk our path through life as a way of the cross, he gives us his mother. During his sufferings she was helplessness personified. She can only be there and remain silent. But her helpless presence gave the Crucified One the greatest joy, the greatest consolation. The same presence gives each of her children the greatest consolation in every suffering. She helps us to recognize the redemptive power of helpless compassion and to enter into the spirit of sacrifice.

> Man's life consists of three parts: preparation for work, the work, and suffering. Some here in Niepokalanow are only preparing themselves, others are already working, and an old gray head like the one sitting in front of you is already passing over to the last part, to suffering. Through these three stages God draws us to himself. The more fervently devoted a soul is to God, the earlier it prepares itself for this third stage, so as to confirm its love for the Immaculata with suffering borne out of love. For nothing unites us so much with the Immaculata and strengthens us in charity than love itself, combined with suffering out of love. Precisely on this way of suffering we can tell whether we really belong to her

unreservedly. In this third stage we must demonstrate the greatest love for her, the love of a knight! And so we must suffer, work and die like a knight, but not an ordinary death. Why not a bullet in the brain to seal one's love for the Immaculata, to shed one's blood as a knight to the last drop, so as to hasten the conquest of the whole world for her?! That is what I wish for myself and for you, too."[164]

Queen of Martyrs.

When Mary is called "Queen of Martyrs", it is because she regally preceded all her suffering children, so as to provide them with mother's milk, so to speak, with the strength to walk their way of the cross with her, through her, and in her.

> Can anyone imagine a more terrible spiritual torment than Mary's compassion during the crucifixion of her son? his fear and affliction were a sword that pierced her heart, as Simeon had prophesied at the presentation of Jesus in the temple. If our Lord himself in Gethsemani found the prospect of his sufferings so unbearable that it wrung drops of blood from him and his soul convulsed his sacred body, then this gives us an image of the extent to which Mary's spiritual pain affected her body and caused her martyrdom. Mary's heart and soul must have melted away as she stood beneath the cross of her son and when at last the lifeless body was placed upon her lap. Therefore, because of the torments that she suffered in her body and soul, she can rightly be called the Queen of Martyrs.[165]

The interior nature of Mary's suffering, which began on the day of the angel's Annunciation and did not end

164. Conference dated August 28, 1939, KMK p. 326.

165. Cardinal John Henry Newman, *Sermons for the Month of May*, cited in C. Kammer, *Die Lauretanische Litanei* (Innsbruck, 1960), p.

until Easter morning, sheds a new light on our understanding of our own path through life as a sacrificial way.

> From the hour of the Annunciation, a terrible, impenetrable darkness shrouded her life, of which she became increasingly aware from month to month. She knew that the future concealed unspeakable sufferings, but she did not know what or when they would be. Yet she knew the words of the prophet, the image of the Messiah as the Man of Sorrows, and, therefore, as the wisest of all virgins, she immediately understood at the Annunciation by the angel that the child would be a child of sorrow. Aged Simeon confirmed this knowledge with unprecedented impact: he would be a sign of contradiction; her soul would be pierced by a sword. The twelve-year-old boy with his puzzling behavior and his majestic answer veils the threatening future even more darkly. The years of his public ministry bring her increasing interior distress about the ultimate outcome, which Jesus' predictions suggest in bleak outline. Mary's path through life passed through incomparable darkness. Why should the Queen of Martyrs bear this dark uncertainty as a cross throughout her life? During his entire life, the King of Martyrs saw the terrible end looming before him, as clear as a vision, and, with his head held high, he made his way to Jerusalem. In this he stood on a plane that was far above all human paths. Yet the ordinary human fate that causes the poor human heart to constrict so horribly, the onward march into the darkness, was to find its example and its source of consolation in the mystery of redemption as well, and probably for this reason the spouse of the Spirit had to endure this suffering at his side. It is the heroism of abandonment to the uncertain will of the Most High. For Mary, too, the darkness was lightened on Golgotha when she recognized her last sacrificial duty: to offer up the most

precious of all precious gifts, the Price of Redemption which also belonged to her as her own possession, and to have it brutally taken away from her. The Crucified who hung there before her eyes was the spotless lamb of sacrifice, to whom she had given the pure and beautiful body that was now so disfigured. In the harmony of his disposition and spiritual gifts, in his strength and gentleness, he is the ideal image of human perfection; she saw this miracle unfold and extended to him a maternal hand as he walked the paths of his childhood. And now that he has reached the state of magnificent manhood, she gives him away as an offering, says her Yes to the immolation of this precious sacrifice, freely consents to this loss, which is unimaginably bitter to her. Thus she accomplishes a heretofore unprecedented regal act of heroic greatness: in union with the King of Sorrows, she turns sorrow itself to the greater glory of God, for the enrichment of the world.[166]

Love of the Cross

Thus the Sorrowful, Immaculate Heart of Mary gives us a love for the cross.

We should reflect that love lives and is nourished by sacrifices. Let us thank the Immaculata for the inner peace, for the delights of love, but let us not forget that all this, although good and beautiful, is not the essence of love and that love can exist without all these feelings, and only then is it perfect love. Its summit is that state in which the Lord Jesus prayed on the cross, 'My God, My God, why hast Thou forsaken Me?' Without sacrifices there is no love. Sacrifices of the senses, especially of the eyes, taste, and hearing, but especially sacrifices of the understanding and the will in holy obedience. Like the love of the Immaculata, like the love of the divine

166. P. Sträter, *Maria in der Glaubenwissenschaft* (Paderborn, 1962), p. 339.

> goodness in her, of the godly heart in her, this love should surround and permeate us, and then sacrifices become a necessity for the soul. Then the soul constantly wants to present new and ever deeper proofs of its love, and these proofs are none other than sacrifices. So I wish for all and for myself as many sacrifices as possible.[167]

We must understand in the divine light that the first moments of zeal, that eagle's flight of the soul toward God, that sweet presence of Jesus, have very little value in God's sight. For those were only God's sweet bonbons, extraordinary graces through which the heavenly Father moved our feelings and drew us to himself. God gave us something of his sweetness to savor, so that we might joyfully and willingly enter upon the path of perfection. For eternal life, however, those days have little merit, for they lacked sacrifices, and efforts on our part. Charity, the 'bond of perfection', is nourished and satisfied only by suffering, sacrifices and the cross. Of course we must be very grateful to God for these, his priceless graces, which were necessary to our great misery and weakness in that first stage of the spiritual life. But when he takes these consolations away from us and sends us painful crosses and sufferings instead, he does not diminish his love in the least. Love for God is perfected in suffering, as gold is purified in the fire.[168]

> How short is life, how fast time flies! Let us sell it, or rather, let us give it away, sacrifice it, and do so as dearly as possible. The more suffering, the better, for after death we can suffer no more. The time for us to prove our love is short, and we only live once![169]

167. Letter to Mugenzai no Sono dated April 9, 1933, BMK, p. 183.
168. Conference from the year1937, KMK, pp. 189-191.
169. Letter to the Brothers in Lviv [Lemberg] dated March 17, 1933.

Chapter Six

The Return of Creation at the End of Time Through the Immaculata

Through Mary the salvation of the world began; through Mary it will also be perfected. We have seen how God's *actio* through the whole history of the Church, but especially in the latter times, permeates the world through the personal interventions of the Immaculata, strengthening and encouraging souls. These are the streams of "grace and mercy" which, in the vision of Tuy, flowed from the pierced hands of the Crucified through the heart of the Immaculata and into souls. We should consider now the reaction, the response that we owe to the Immaculata. In her first apparition at Fatima, Mary asked the children, "Do you want to offer yourselves to God, so as to endure all the sufferings that he would like to send you, in reparation for the sins by which he is offended and as an entreaty for the conversion of sinners?" Their answer came immediately: "Yes, we want to!"[170]

170. SLF, p. 169.

The Apostles of the End Times

Saint Louis Marie de Montfort gives to those who consecrate themselves completely and utterly to the mother of God in these end times a special name, "apostles of the end times", and he describes the manner of their response, their qualities, and the disposition of their hearts. In doing so he is quite aware of the role of the Immaculata in the final battle. It is a question of mankind's return to God in a particular hour of human history, namely the last hour. Jesus' discourses about the *parousia*, various passages in the epistles, and especially the *Book of Revelation* disclose these times to us as the apotheosis of Satan's power, his last rebellion. In the midst of the seemingly total victory of the adversary appears the "King of kings, the Lord of lords", who brings about the final victory, who immediately inaugurates the Last Judgment and eternity. It is only logical if the Immaculata occupies the central role in the work of creation and redemption, as has been demonstrated thus far, if she is the way by which God comes down to us and the way by which we return to God, for the most important stage of this journey, after all, is still the final one. And since we are evidently standing in the middle of this stage, it is important to know how the Christian who finds himself in the final battle must be especially imbued with Mary.

The first mark of the true Christian in the end time is the apostolic spirit. At Fatima the mother of God herself trained the little children to be apostles by snatching them away from their "private" personal religious life and placing them in the midst of the greatest concerns for souls, for the Church, and for the whole world. Two hundred years earlier, Saint Louis Marie foresaw how the "servants, slaves, and children of Mary" would go out into the world to preach true devotion to

Mary and thus crush the head of the devil. "They will be like thunderclouds, which fly abroad at the slightest breath of the Holy Ghost so as to shower down the rain of God's word and of eternal life." Saint Maximilian Kolbe describes more precisely the exact relationship between the apostles and our Lady, who calls and sends them: we are knights of the Immaculata, instruments in her immaculate hands, *i.e.,* completely dependent upon her and entirely subordinate to her will, like a paint-brush in the hand of the artist.[171]

This mission as knights and apostles of the Immaculata takes shape concretely as participation in the final struggle, the decisive battle in the end times between the devil and the Immaculata, who crushes the devil's head. The "plunder" that is at stake consists of souls. Not by accident did Mary show the children of Fatima a vision of hell and the souls that go there as though in a whirlwind. The whole message of Fatima is a mother's cry of alarm, which shows her children the great danger and tries to save them from it. The apparition on July 13 describes the apotheosis, the almost total victory of Satan through his accomplices, the materialistic atheism that rules the world. Opposing this is the Immaculate Heart of Mary as the sole escape given by God and the sure victory.

Saint Louis Marie clearly points out that this battle is a terrible one.

> Lastly, Mary must become as terrible as an army in battle array (*Cant.* 6:3) to the devil and his followers, especially in these latter times. For Satan, knowing that he has little time (*Apoc.* 12:12)—even less than ever—to destroy souls, intensifies his efforts and his onslaughts every day. He will not hesitate to stir up

171. Concerning the nature of the Knighthood of the Immaculata, see Fr. Karl Stehlin, *The Immaculata, Our Ideal* (Angelus Publishing, 2006?), pp. GT49-58[English text page numbers?].

savage persecutions and set treacherous snares for Mary's faithful servants and children whom he finds more difficult to overcome than others. It is chiefly in reference to these last wicked persecutions of the devil, daily increasing until the advent of the reign of anti-Christ, that we should understand that first and well-known prophecy and curse of God uttered against the serpent in the garden of paradise.... 'I will place enmities between you and the Woman.' "[172]

For this reason the apostles of the mother of God will be a sign of contradiction.

> They will bring to the poor and the lowly everywhere the sweet fragrance of Jesus, but they will bring the odor of death to the great, the rich, and the proud of this world. They will be like thunder-clouds flying through the air at the slightest breath of the Holy Ghost. Attached to nothing, surprised at nothing, troubled at nothing, they will shower down the rain of God's word and of eternal life. They will thunder against sin, they will storm against the world, they will strike down the devil and his followers, and, for life or for death, they will pierce through and through with the two-edged sword of God's word all those against whom they are sent by almighty God.[173]

Saint Maximilian defines the knighthood of the Immaculata as "striving for the conversion of sinners, heretics, schismatics, Jews, etc., especially Freemasons; and for the sanctification of all, under the protection and through the intercession of the Immaculata".[174] "Our desire is not only that we ourselves be consecrated without reservations to the Immaculata, but also that all the souls in the whole world, those who exist now and those that are yet to come, might consecrate themselves

172. *True Devotion*, paragraphs 50(g)-51, p. 22.
173. *Ibid.*, paragraphs 56-57, p. 25.
174. Diploma of the *Militia Immaculatae.*

to her entirely and unreservedly."[175] Even though our own return to God, our personal sanctification, must take first place, the missionary spirit is also part of our Christian life (this is the special grace of the sacrament of Confirmation). Yet this is again especially true for us who are living in the apocalyptic times. For Saint Maximilian, the apocalyptic final struggle is simply one last challenge, in which the Immaculata conquers the world for Christ, or better: in which the Immaculata herself definitively crushes the devil's head in us and through us.

> We must win the whole world and each individual soul for the Immaculata, now and in the future and until the end of the world, and through her—for the Sacred Heart of Jesus. And then we must make sure that the banner of the Immaculata is not snatched from any soul, but instead that souls acquire a deeper love for her and that the bond of love between her and souls is strengthened, so that souls become increasingly one with her and only with her. In this way she alone, the Immaculata, can live and love and act in these souls and through them. Just as the Immaculata belongs to Jesus and is God's own possession, so too every soul will belong to Jesus, to God through her and in her, much more thoroughly and better than without her . . . to the extent possible. But then these souls will manage to love the Sacred Heart of Jesus much more than before. Like the Immaculata, they too will plunge into the depths of his love, into the cross and the Eucharist, much better than before. Through her the divine Love will kindle its fire in the world and consume the world. And then the 'assimilation of souls through love' will take place. But when will this divinization of the world in and through the Immaculata take place? . . For that it is necessary that she, she alone work [in souls] and that those who consecrate themselves to

175. Letter to P. Florian Koziura dated April 29, 1931, BMK, pp. 235-236.

> her give themselves unreservedly, that they first belong to her, that they deepen this devotion boundlessly, that they fasten this bond of love ever closer, until their souls are completely imbued with it. This is the absolutely indispensable condition. Mary will work in them to the extent to which they belong to her. And finally there will be nothing more of their very own in them. Then they will be unreservedly her property.[176]

THE FINAL STRUGGLE UNDER THE BANNER OF THE IMMACULATA

The ends times are even more clearly described as "the great apostasy of the nations". Falling away from the Faith is the worst possible thing, because thereby souls are turned away from God and the true goal of their lives and they are lost in error and sin. In his seraphic prayer, Saint Louis Marie de Montfort describes this situation of the end times:

> they have transgressed thy divine law, they have abandoned the Gospel, the torrents of wickedness flood the whole world and sweep even thy servants away with them. Unbelief sits enthroned, thy sanctuary is desecrated and the abomination of desolation is in the holy place.[177]

Opposed to this triumph of Satan is the "great sign in heaven, the Woman clothed with the sun". Mary is the protectress of our faith: to her God assigns the task of disclosing Satan's whole strategy to her children .

Especially at La Salette, the unprecedented extent of the diabolical attack is strikingly set before our eyes.

> Many will turn their backs on the Faith; the number of priests and religious who fall away from the true religion will be large. There will even be bishops among them.... [The demons] will subvert the faith

176. Diary entry dated April 23, 1933, BMK, pp. 460-461.
177. LGM, p. 676.

> even among consecrated persons and blind them so much that these persons [with a few exceptions by a special grace] will accept the spirit of the fallen angels. Many religious houses will lose the faith completely and lead many souls to ruin. Bad books will flood the world and the spirits of darkness will spread general laxity in the service of God everywhere. They will have great power over nature. Churches in the service of the fallen angels will spring up. They will enthrall people, even clergymen, for the latter will no longer be guided by the spirit of the Gospel, which is a spirit of humility, love, and zeal for God's honor. Unusual happenings will occur everywhere, for the true Faith will have been extinguished and a false light will enlighten the world.... The precursor of the Antichrist, with the armies of many peoples, will wage battle against the true Christ, the sole Redeemer of the world. The former will spill much blood and try to destroy the true worship of God so as to make men worship himself as God.... But before this happens, a sort of false peace will prevail in the world; people will think of nothing but their own amusement. The wicked will allow themselves to commit every sort of sin. But the children of Holy Church, the children of faith, my authentic imitators, will grow in the love of God and in the virtues that are dearest to me.... Rome will lose the faith and become the seat of the Antichrist. The demons of the air will work with the Antichrist great signs on earth and in heaven, and people will become more and more perverted. But God will take care of his faithful servants and men of good will....[178]

At the same time Mary gathers her loyal children about her, for to her has been given the power to crush the devil's head in these end times.

178. J. M. Höcht, *Die grosse Botschaft von La Salette* (Stein am Rhein, 1990), pp. 56-63; A. de Lassus, *Le Secret de Notre Dame à La Salette* (Paris: Action Familiale et Scolaire, No. 125, 1996).

I turn to the world with an urgent appeal; I call the true disciples of the living God who reigns in heaven, of the one true Redeemer of mankind; I call the true followers of Christ, who became man; I call my children, my true devotees, who have given themselves to me entirely, so that I may lead them to my divine son; [I call] those whom I carry in my arms, so to speak, who live according to my spirit; finally I call the apostles of the end times, the true disciples of Christ, who—despising the world and themselves—live in poverty and humility, in silence and obscurity, in prayer and penance, in purity and union with God, in suffering, unknown to the world. The time has come that they appear and bring light to the world. Go and manifest yourselves as my beloved children. I am with you and in you, so that your faith may be the light than will enlighten you in these unfortunate days.[179]

Sister Lucia of Fatima presents the Immaculate Heart of Mary to the world as the final means of salvation to bring souls home to God in these end times.

The devil is arming himself for the decisive battle against the Virgin Mary. And because he knows what offends God most and what it takes to win the greatest number of souls, he does his utmost to win over consecrated souls, for in that way he gains access to large fields of souls, so as to conquer them more easily.... Father, the mother of God did not tell me explicitly that we are in the end times, but she gave me to understand as much for three reasons:

First, because she told me that the devil is preparing for the decisive battle against the mother of God; but the decisive battle is the final battle, wherein is manifested which side will have the victory and which will be defeated.

179. A. de Lassus, *op. cit.*, p. 35.

> Second, because she told my cousins and me that God is now giving the world the two last means of salvation: the rosary and the devotion to the Immaculate Heart of Mary. But if these are the last means of salvation, that implies that there will be no more besides.
>
> Third, because it is in keeping with the plans of divine Providence that, if God is to punish the world, all the ordinary means of conversion be exhausted first. But when he saw that the world neglected all these means, he offered it the last means of salvation, namely his most holy mother. But if we despise and reject this last means of salvation, too, then there is no more forgiveness for us, because then we have committed the sin that the Gospel calls the sin against the Holy Ghost.[180]

Again and again Sister Lucia speaks in her letters about the "diabolical wave that is sweeping over the world", about the "loss of the clear path", about "the deceit of the demons and their accomplices", about the "false teachings that deceive men".[181]

> The devil has succeeded in planting evil under the protective mantle of good, and blind men busy themselves leading others, as our Lord says in the Gospel, and souls allow themselves to be deceived. I gladly sacrifice to God my life for the peace of his Church, for priests, and for all consecrated souls, especially for those who are so much deceived and stray from the true way.[182]

And precisely in these most difficult hours, our knowledge about the Immaculata fills us with great joy.

180. J. M. Alonso CMF, *La Verdad sobre el Secreto do Fatima* (Madrid, 1976), pp. 103-106.

181. Br. Michel de la Trinité, *Toute la vérité sur Fatima*, vol. III (Saint-Parres-les-Vaudes, 1985), pp. 507-510.

182. Letter dated September 16, 1970, in: P. S. Martins dos Reis, *Uma Vida ao servico de Fatima* (Porto, 1973), pp. 377-379.

> I always think about the great promise that fills me with joy: 'I will never leave you alone. My Immaculate Heart will be your refuge and the way that leads you to God.' I believe that this promise was not given for me alone, but for all the souls that flee to the heart of their heavenly mother and allow themselves to be guided along the ways that she has designated.[183]

A twofold *leitmotif* runs through Saint Maximilian Kolbe's writings to his *Militia Immaculatae*: "She will crush the devil's head," and "You alone have conquered all heresies throughout the world." He thereby clearly indicates that the final battle in preserving the true faith and overcoming errors will be decided by the Immaculata, who precisely in this way will definitively crush Satan's head.

> Now that the evil spirit is not waiting but working swiftly according to plan, we cannot relent for any reason in our efforts in the City of the Immaculata: after all, souls are at stake and the conquest of the whole world and of every individual soul for the Immaculata, and the sanctification of all souls through the Immaculata until the end of time. It would really be a shame for even one soul to be lost.[184]

Now there is something particularly and inherently dangerous about this final battle. The horrors of apostasy and the countless sins crying out to heaven are certainly the results of the wicked foe's triumphs, but it would be a big mistake to think that that was the essence of the diabolical attack. No, these phenomena are only the visible consequences, the tip of the iceberg. If that were all that the enemy had to offer, he

183. Letter dated April 14, 1945, in: A. M. Martins, S.J., *Fatima e o Coracao de Maria* (Sao Paulo, 1984), pp. 62-63.
184. *Do ideału MI* (Niepokalanów, 1996), p. 77.

would be easy to fight. Yet the real "abomination of desolation" consists of a mentality, an atmosphere, an attitude toward life: the air is infected and poisoned by a spirit that considers secularity, the things of this world, to be the essence of human existence. Imperceptibly it permeates a human being with a thorough over-emphasis on one's own self, one's own short life on earth, one's own freedom. Through a comprehensive propaganda that has been going on for two hundred years now, the enemy has created an atmosphere of religious indifference which grips even the best believers, since they ceaselessly breathe in this spirit and no longer or rarely are aware of its poison. The generation after the Second Vatican Council is especially affected by this poison, because they were born into a time when people no longer have had to fight. This poison works on two levels. On the one level it leads a person to a superficial, routine, and habitual attitude toward the truth and the glories of our Faith; on the other level it leads to an equally superficial and trivializing position with regard to the lures and temptations of the enemy. Thus good becomes boring and evil attractive. But who will puncture these two levels of superficiality and lead these endangered people to a deep recognition both of the divine truths and also of horrible temptations? Only the Immaculata! The great Marian saints have realized this very well and therefore have aroused hosts of Christians from their fatal lethargy to serve under Mary's banner. Precisely because there are no other means of instilling zeal in souls (such as the example of saintly people, Catholic civilization, inspiring literature, art, theater, and music, or even an attractive Marian movement, etc.), God lets us know that, besides all these ordinary means of fostering a

Christian life, the Immaculate Heart of Mary is being given to us in these end times to be our "final refuge and the way that leads us to God". And why does God want this? Probably in order to show the world the power of his masterpiece, that Mary "has overcome all heresies throughout the world" and also that she alone "will crush the devil's head".

Chapter Seven

World Without End

Dying in Mary

"The time is short.... For the fashion [form] of this world passeth away" (*1 Cor.* 7:29, 31). As the great hour draws near, the soul thinks with bitterness and sorrow about the years that it has spent in sin, about the many wasted graces. Created in order to reach the highest summit of sanctity in this valley of tears, the soul has become bogged down in lukewarmness or even in evil. How few times there have been of zeal and fidelity! Were God's many proofs of his grace in vain? So man stands trembling in the evening of his life: "If Thou, O Lord, wilt mark iniquities, Lord, who shall stand it?" (*Ps.* 29). So as not to lose heart in this decisive hour, Christ gives us a twofold grace: the sacrament of Extreme Unction to accompany us on our journey home and the Immaculata, the Gate of Heaven.

The Last Sacrament with Mary

The Anointing of the Sick prepares the Christian for the final battle, for the hour of our death. It is the final purification of the senses and the mind, brought about by Christ himself. The many sins that we have committed with our senses have spread through our whole being like leprosy. Therefore the anointing of the five senses brings about this purification that only the Good Samaritan can accomplish. Only through his blood can man come into God's presence purified. But the powers of the soul must be purified, too: our whole interior life, understanding, will, and emotions. The lower powers of the soul must be subjected again to the higher powers, but above all the soul itself must be freed from all the attachments, from everything that is superficial and fleeting. Christ enters the inmost part of the soul in order to direct it to God alone and to orient it entirely toward what is eternal and lasting. This great sacramental grace of one's last hours can be effective, however, only if the soul also believes in it, submits itself, and is ready to allow this last great operation to be performed upon it. The presence of the Immaculata "at the hour of our death" makes it possible for man to obtain the grace of a holy death. Now that it is reaching its destination, the Immaculata stirs up in the soul all the ardent love of her heart. Her presence is the sole guarantee that Christ will gain admission to the most hidden chambers of the heart. For we have been accustomed our whole life long to keeping our doors more or less closed and, if it were up to us, we would not suddenly overcome the habit at this moment. She, however, is called the "Gate of Heaven". Her presence, which is totally devoted to God, her power of communicating grace, her intercessory omnipotence, compels, as it were, the old man to flee and crushes the head of every obstacle ... and all the doors are opened for the final purification.

That is why the hour of death is also the moment of the final, decisive battle. The more or less ingrained "old Adam" with his habits and self-centeredness hampers the soul and traps it in base concerns. But since Mary is the new Eve and has overcome the curse of the old Adam and the first Eve, she will do this again in the soul that is devoted to her. More precisely, she will communicate in its fullness the stream of Christ's graces, which in this sacrament constitute a participation in the victorious power of the Risen Lord. Thus the soul that is in the throes of death will find in her "a refuge and the way that leads to God". Moreover, since the moment of death decides between heaven and hell, the devil and his cohorts will pull out all the stops in order to mislead the soul into despair or unwillingness to repent. That is why this hour in particular is the high point of the constant battle between the Immaculata and the devil. Then he experiences his ultimate defeat, then she will crush his head, so that he must leave the soul.

Mary, the Example of a Holy Departure from This Life.

The Immaculata gave a motherly example for every moment and every situation of our life and is our example and prototype in everything; this is true too for the hour of our death. According to the general opinion of the Church fathers and theologians, Mary accepted death, even though, being sinless, she was not subject to the law of death. This was so chiefly for two reasons. First, as the new Eve, she wanted to be like the new Adam in everything and to atone with him as co-Redemptrix by being united with his sufferings to the very end. Secondly, she wanted to go before us as our supernatural mother. Would it have been right for her, the mother who watches us all struggle with death, to be the only one to escape death? We often see death only as robbery, loss, and defeat. From the example of the saints, however, and especially from her, we learn that it is the best sacrifice of adoration and love that we can offer to God. For death demands the total giving of oneself, the utmost faith in God's power, boundless hope, and ardent love.

Thus Mary gives us the greatest possible understanding of the mystery of our passage from time over into eternity: in the opinion of the Church fathers, Mary's departure was brought about by her great love.

> Not only inasmuch as she voluntarily yearned to suffer death, out of love for conformity with her son and with us, but even more because her love and longing for the eternal heritage of God, and especially of her heavenly son, had become so intense that it burst the bonds of her body and released her soul to go to heaven in an ecstasy of love. Such an occurrence is quite plausible, since we know that the soul of many a mystic, for instance Saint Paul, was snatched up to heaven even during his lifetime and seemed scarcely united with his body. In Mary's case it is easy to conclude that the overwhelming force of her ecstasy of love snapped the last remaining thread that kept her soul and body together. Thus her death became a burnt offering of love, a love-death resplendent with the utmost solemnity and sanctity, which is why the Church's terminology wisely refers to Mary's departure from this life as a *dormitio*, as a falling asleep.[185]

The Grace of Final Perseverance

From the very first moment, the soul has received everything from Mary, and in Mary the soul will also finish the race. The one who has begun the work will also complete it. This completion of the individual life occurs at death. It is the final step of the long way home to God, the gateway to eternity. The presence of the Immaculata is most important precisely in this hour of the last battle and the definitive decision.

185. M. J. Scheeben, *Katholische Dogmatik*, vol. 3, p. 576.

> I imagine how I will stand there naked before the assembly of angels and of men. I turn hither and yon, in order to see with my mind's eye whether I might find a helper, someone who would intercede for me. But I have found that thou alone can save me by thine intercession. And I know that thou wilt never depart from me.[186]

Confident of this, the soul prays many thousands of times: "now and at the hour of our death". The Mediatrix of All Graces is also the mediatrix of the greatest, most undeserved grace of final perseverance. The artist perfects his work. In what hour did Christ give her to us as our mother? At the hour of his death! Isn't that an indication that Mary is always our mother, but most of all when we most resemble him, namely at the hour of death? Isn't it the greatest consolation to have the privilege then of hearing the words: "Behold thy mother"?!

> He gives her to me as a mother. And now that he has returned to the Father and has put me in his place, so that I might complete by my suffering what is still lacking in his passion for his body, the Church, the Virgin is there again to teach me to suffer as he did, to let me hear the last words of his soul, which no one could understand except for her, his mother. Then, when I have spoken my *'consummatum est'* [it is accomplished], she, the Gate of Heaven, will lead me into the heavenly courts and whisper to me in secret the mysterious words, 'I rejoiced when they said unto me, let us go into the house of the Lord' (*Ps*. 121:1).[187]

186. Ethiopian Liturgy, "Harp of Mary", cited in: P. Sträter, S.J., *Maria in der Offenbarung* (Paderborn, 1962), p. 135.
187. Bl. Elisabeth de la Trinité, Final Retreat, August 1906, in: P. Philipon, *La doctrine spirituelle de Soeur Elisabeth de la Trinité* (Bruges, 1938), p. 192.

The End of the World in Light of the Immaculata

"He will come again in glory to judge the living and the dead, and his kingdom will have no end." The all-pervasive light of this glory, which will someday become for the blessed a participation in the inexhaustible light of the divine life, brings to light all thoughts, words, and deeds at the Last Judgment and reveals them in the presence of all creation. Christ's second coming and his judgment are expressions of his kingship. Mary, as Queen, participates in this dominion. Now the Last Judgment is the exercise of the authority of the world's Judge over all the moral acts of creatures. But it is also an exercise of the Queen's authority, that is, the manifestation of her maternal and queenly influence on mankind. At the end of the world it will become evident how much we owe to her; the Last Judgment will be a brilliant triumph of Mary over the devil and all evil, a revelation to the whole world of her intercessory omnipotence and her mercy.

The Great Promises of the Immaculata

This special distinction of the Immaculata at the end of the world is evident in the promises with which Mary assures her faithful children. They shed a special light on God's Providence, and these extraordinary promises also suggest how well pleased God is with Mary. These great promises are also the best proof of God's will to manifest to all the world the preeminent importance of his masterpiece. Among all graces there is one that no human being can merit and which is always a sheer act of God's mercy, namely the grace of final perseverance. If not even the holiest life on earth and all the sacrifices of mankind taken together can merit this grace, then we stand in astonishment before the fact that God gave precisely this greatest of all graces to the Immaculata to be, as it were, her own. With even greater astonishment we must realize that Mary grants this greatest of all graces with such liberality that it requires only a small gesture on our part in order to receive it. This gesture is nothing other than the expression of our devotion to her. Thus the wearing of the Scapular of our Lady of Mount Carmel is connected with the promise that "whoever dies wearing this habit will be preserved from the fires of hell," and whoever performs a few additional practices "will be released from the torments of Purgatory on the Saturday after his death".[188] The mother of God gives similar promises to those who revere the Holy rosary. To Blessed Alan de la Roche she revealed that:

> The soul that confidently seeks refuge in me through my rosary will not be lost. All who devoutly pray the rosary while meditating on the mysteries will not be cast down by misfortune and will be preserved from an unforeseen death. If they are in sin, then they will obtain the grace of conversion; they will obtain the grace of perseverance, however, if they are righteous, and they will have a share in life everlasting.[189]

The Immaculate Heart of Mary promised this same grace at Fatima: "I promise salvation to anyone who practices this devotion [to my Immaculate Heart]. These souls are especially loved by God, like flowers that I have planted in order to adorn his throne" [Fatima, June 13, 1917]. To those who practice this devotion she promises "to assist them at the hour of death with all the graces necessary for their salvation" (Pontevedra, December 12, 1925).

188. *Le Scapulaire du Mont-Carmel* (Flavigny-sur-Ozerain, 2001), p. 15 and p. 19.
189. Cited in Saint Ludwig M. Grignion de Montfort, *Der Heilige Rosenkranz* (Feldkirch, 1980), p. 152.

"And after our exile, show us Jesus."

The end of the ages is also the end of the exile of the children of Eve. Then he who is Lord over life and death will manifest himself upon the clouds of heaven. The Church teaches us, however, that Mary guides her faithful children to the Lord who is to come: "and after this, our exile, show unto us the blessed fruit of thy womb, Jesus." Therefore, when that great day, that terrible day of wrath dawns (*dies irae, dies illa*),

> . . . then we, too, will have to thank her for this final, magnificent grace for the whole world. She prepared for his first coming, and from her proceeded the preparation of the few other people who knew about it: Joseph and John, Elizabeth and Zachary. And no one else will be able to prepare the second coming, as well. She must help us. For it is still her son who will come then. She will give him a second time to the world, this time for complete deliverance and his final triumph. No longer for the cross and suffering.... Then the banishment of the children of Eve will come to an end. They will return home. Finally every tear will be wiped away.[190]

THE COMPLETED *REACTIO DEI* IN ETERNITY

What is the heaven that has been promised to us? The eternal contemplation of the divine glory and, kindled by this vision, the flame of love, to which there are no more obstacles now. The soul has been conformed to the Immaculata; all restraints and shadows have vanished. Only now does the *actio Dei* find its complete response in the *re-actio* of the creature which has arrived at its destination. But what is it like, our everlasting answer to God's Word to us, our *reditus, refluxus* — the

190. Josef Dillersberger, *Die Stimme deines Grusses* (Salzburg, 1936), pp. 146-147.

return that we make — to the perpetual gift of divine love in glory? Here on earth this always remains an incomprehensible mystery, for "eye hath not seen, nor ear heard, neither hath it entered into the heart of man, what things God hath prepared for them that love him." How could we understand today how it is possible to "be filled unto all the fullness of God" (*Eph.* 3:19), namely, to participate in the limitless ocean of divine love?! And the Immaculata? "We are always and above all else her property, in heaven as well." For where she is, there is our place, too, not due to our merits, but because we are the property of the Immaculata. In heaven, too, Mary remains the Mediatrix of All Graces, and thus of all divine life. Therefore we can say that our heavenly bliss is the eternal gift of God's infinite love, in and through the Immaculata! After all, she is not only Queen of earth, of the universe, but also Queen of heaven, the Queen of love, which is perfect participation in God, since God is Love!

This heavenly happiness is participation in God's nature, admission into the family of the most Holy Trinity. If we "see God as he is", then it will also become visible who we are in God's sight. If we are not to be completely blinded by this mystery, God must enable us to behold this abundance of his glory. Therefore he instills in us a light which infinitely develops the light of reason and of faith: the light of glory, *lumen gloriae*, which enables us to see God himself and allows us to bear the ecstasy of dwelling within the endless life of the Trinity. But since Mary possesses the fullness of graces and is their universal mediatrix, can we not also assume that she grants us this light of glory? The bride of the Lamb, the mother, prepares her children for the eternal wedding banquet, clothes them with the appropriate garments, enables them to take part in the eternal festival, makes them full citizens of the heavenly city, the eternal Jerusalem. The Church corroborates this when she applies to Mary the passages about eternal Wisdom: "He that shall find me shall find life and shall have salvation from the Lord" (*Prov.* 8:35). "They that explain [proclaim, glorify] me shall have life everlasting" (*Ecclu.* 24:31). "For wisdom is more active than all active things and reacheth everywhere by reason of her purity. For she is a vapor of the power of God, and a certain pure emanation of the glory of the almighty God.... For she is the brightness of eternal light, and the unspotted mirror of God's majesty, and the image of his goodness" (*Wis.* 7:24-26). According to Saint Thomas Aquinas, wisdom is the science that sees everything in the light of the highest causes. The perfection of this light, however, is the *lumen gloriae*. Could we not conclude from this that the Immaculata receives this *lumen gloriae* perfectly in her heart and radiates it to all the blessed? Or, to put it another way, might God not have willed that the eternally radiant Immaculate Heart, as the "Seat of Wisdom", be in heaven completely and utterly the "Cause of our joy" and of everlasting, infinite happiness, which consists of the beatific vision? Instead of beholding the eternal realities with our earthly eyes, we will discover God in his inmost nature in this light, and all created things in him.

Eternal joy, however, is not only contemplation but also love without end. And since all of God's love and all the love of creation have been united in this heart through the fact that Mary is the spouse of the Holy Ghost, eternal happiness consists also in endless and highest possible participation in the love of this heart, in the loving bond of the Blessed Trinity, which is entirely focused on this Immaculate Heart. "Father, I will that where I am, they also whom thou hast given me may be with me: that they may see my glory which thou hast given me, because thou hast loved me before the creation of the world" (Jn 17:24). But where is Christ? With the Father, but also and forever one with his mother.

Not only does the soul return to God in eternity, but the body also shares in the beauties of heavenly glory. Now, however, the purpose of all creation has been fulfilled in the mystery of Jesus and Mary, that is, in the mystery of Christ's Incarnation through Mary and his Redemption with Mary. All other creatures share in this mystery. Consequently the definitive triumph in heaven at the resurrection of the body consists in the definitive entrance of the elect into the eternal union of the Lamb and the bride. And since this mystery of love in the eternal banquet involves the body also, the splendors of the glorified body of Christ redound to Mary and from her to every risen body: "And behold, I saw a new heaven and a new earth" (*Apoc.* 21:1). Her capacity as Queen of the universe finds its perfection here: full of the substantial, divine, eternal light, having the fullness of divine life. Like a sun she illumines the angels and saints, and she communicates divine life down to the last atom and the last fiber of the risen body of each one of the elect. Here her motherhood also attains perfection, since she can now grant everything to her beloved children.

"Come and I will show thee the bride, the wife of the Lamb. And he took me up in spirit to a great and high mountain: and he showed me the holy city Jerusalem, coming down out of heaven from God, having the glory of God. And the light thereof was like to a precious stone, as to the jasper stone even as crystal" (*Apoc.* 21:9-11).

"And I saw no temple therein. For the Lord God Almighty is the temple thereof, and the Lamb. And the city hath no need of the sun, nor of the moon, to shine in it. For the glory of God hath enlightened it: and the Lamb is the lamp thereof. And the nations shall walk in the light of it.... And they shall bring the glory and honor of the nations into it. There shall not enter into it any thing defiled or that worketh abomination or maketh a lie: but they that are written in the book of life of the Lamb" (*Apoc.* 21:22-27).

"This city which mankind will find at the end of the world so as to convert and to satisfy their hunger for righteousness—this city is the most Blessed Virgin, who is called by the Holy Ghost: the city and dwelling place of God."[191]

191. LGM, p. 513.

Part Four

The Immaculata in the Mystery of the Most Holy Trinity

Introduction to Part Four

It has been our privilege to contemplate the marvel of the triune God in his infinite love for his creatures. The missions of the second and third divine persons have opened up the depths of God to our view. But with astonishment we have discovered that there is one creature to which the triune God has connected his entire revelation, his entire work *ad extra*. This leads us to the conclusion that a special relation to this creature exists in God's inner life as well. All that is creaturely is summed up in God's interior life in the statement: God the Father begets the Son from all eternity, and in this begetting are included all things that are not God, as the shadows or the "garment" of the Only-Begotten. Things do not exist in and of themselves but are only contained in the Word as exemplar, as all the possible imitations of the divine prototype, as all the possible echoes of the one spoken eternal Word. "That which was made in him was life" (*Jn.* 1:3-4) [N.B. This translation is based on an alternative reading of the Vulgate with different punctuation: *quod factum est in ipso vita erat*]. This does not change when all things begin to exist. God's relation to these things is always the same. It is just that things acquire a new relation to God. Whereas before they existed they were ideal, exemplary, present only in God's mind, now they become real. Therefore when the world comes to an end, God will be "all in all", and all immortal beings who have lived according to the will of God shall return to that eternal inner life of God.

Now if it is true that the ideal pattern of every-thing that exists in God, strictly speaking, "is life" and has its exemplary prototype, according to which God will eventually call it into being and, after it has loved faithfully, will unite it with himself in his eternal triune life, then what must the relationship of the Immaculata to the most Holy Trinity look like? Given the fact that on earth she became the mother and associate of the Son, the God-bearer and co-Redemptrix, the spouse of the Holy Ghost and Mediatrix of All divine Graces, what importance must she have then in his innermost life, in the divine processions which are the eternal prototypes and perpetual sources of the missions of the Son and Holy Ghost in the world?

Therefore, in order to contemplate the meaning of the greatest of all creatures and, in her, the most profound meaning of all creation, we must enter into the mystery of God's interior life, insofar as God himself allows us to do so through his revelation. The saints all teach, however, that this requires a special preparation of the heart, *i.e.*, that in this matter one learns much more on one's knees than from the books of the wisest scholars.

Chapter One

The Mystery of the Trinity

When God revealed his inmost nature, He disclosed that it is infinite goodness and eternal love. The first disclosure of God's name in the Old Testament reads: "I AM WHO AM." here he reveals that he is in complete possession of being, that all being belongs to him, that he has being in and of himself (*ipsum esse subsistens*). The perfect disclosure of the divine name in the New Testament reads: "God is love." Yet perfect love requires an I and a Thou and their mutual self-giving. The love is in the beloved. And thus God reveals here that in his nature there are several persons, the Lover, the Beloved, and the Gift of both: the most Holy Trinity. God's goodness consists in the giving and sharing of himself (*bonum diffusivum sui*): all of creation is the act of this divine goodness. But before any sharing outside of himself, from all eternity there is the giving and receiving (*fluxus-refluxus*) of the divine nature itself within the Holy Trinity. And this movement of love is reflected, depicted, and shines forth in the created universe. The purpose of everything created is to testify to God's glory, *i.e.*, to manifest this interior movement of love of the divine persons. In other words: the processions of the divine person within the Trinity are reflected in the missions of the divine persons *ad extra* — outside the Trinity—, and the work of redemption consists precisely of that, namely the return of creation to the Father.

"The Father begets the Son, while the Holy Ghost proceeds from the Father and the Son. In these few words is contained the mystery of the life of the most Holy Trinity and of all the perfections existing in creatures, which are only an echo in a different nature, a hymn of praise in various tonalities, of this first and most beautiful of all mysteries. We also have to make use of words taken from the vocabulary of creatures, because we have no others. Even so, we must always remember that these are very imperfect words.

Who is the Father? What is it that constitutes his being? Begetting, because he begets the Son from all eternity; and for all eternity he continually begets his Son.

Who is the Son? He is the one who is begotten; always and for all eternity he is begotten by the Father.

And who is the Holy Ghost? He is the fruit of love of the Father and the Son. The fruit of a created love is a created conception. Hence the fruit of this love, of the prototype of all created love, can also be nothing else but a conception. Hence the Holy Ghost is an uncreated conception, an eternal one; He is the prototype of every sort of human conception in the universe.

> Thus the Father begets; the Son is begotten; the Holy Ghost proceeds. This is their essence, by which they are distinguished, each one from the others. Their common nature, however, unifies them. Divine existence is their essence.
>
> The Holy Ghost, therefore, is a most holy conception, infinitely holy, immaculate.[192]

The mysterious life of this infinitely perfect divine

192. St. Maximilian Kolbe, Article dated February 17, 1941, BMK, p. 597.

nature is a life of perfect knowledge and love. God knows and loves himself infinitely, and thus the Father (*plenitudo fontalis bonitatis*—the fullness and source of goodness) begets the Son. The Holy Ghost is "spirated" or breathed out; he proceeds from the Father and the Son as the connection (*nexus*), the unity, the union, the oneness-in-being of them both. In the Holy Trinity everything is God the Father or comes from the Father. All comes from the eternal Father and returns to him through the Son and the Holy Ghost. The Father works only through the Son and the Holy Ghost.

Saint Maximilian calls this twofold procession the flowing out (*fluxus*) and the flowing back (*refluxus*) of eternal love. The entire goodness of the divine substance in the Father is in the Son through filiation (the begetting), and the whole mutual love (*mutua caritas*) of the Father and the Son for one another (for the Son is the perfect image of the Father) is the Holy Ghost through his procession from the Father and the Son by way of being breathed out (*spiratio*—spiration). He is the conception of Father and Son, the divine *conceptio*.

These two processions can also be called the unfolding and the folding up of divine love, like a flower that unfolds and then folds up again. Love unfolds from the Father through the Son and the Holy Ghost, and folds up again as the return to the Father through the Holy Ghost and the Son. Within the Trinity the unfolding of divine love is the begetting of the Son, whereas the folding up again is the proceeding of the Holy Ghost. As the seal of the mutual love of Father and Son, the Holy Ghost is God-Love itself, whose characteristic it is to give expression to the essence of divine love; he is the union between Father and Son, the response, the return to the source. God the Father, so to speak, emanates love (the ocean of divinity) by begetting the Son. The

Son is this love as a receptive person (the image of the Father) and his entire personhood is being-directed-to-the-Father (*esse ad Patrem*), and this devotion to the Father is the unfolding. Now the mutual self-giving of the Father and the Son is in turn a person. In the Holy Ghost is accomplished this movement from Father to Son and from Son to Father. He is the seal, the conception of the primordial love of the Father and of the receptive and responsive love of the Son: and so this Love returns to the Father—that is the completion.

In order to make this eternal conception of Father and Son even clearer, Saint Maximilian says that it is untouched, perfect, unspotted, immaculate! Now the term *Immacullata Conceptio* means something positive as a divine perfection. It is one of those expressions which, albeit formulated in a negative way, allow us to say something positive about God; other examples are "unending, boundless, immaterial, uncreated", etc. Similarly, when we speak about "untrodden" or "untouched snow", we mean snow that is white in color, with its unspotted purity and beauty. Thus we can say that God is *immaculatus*: hc is all light, totally beautiful without shadow.

Chapter Two

Who Are You, O Immaculata?

When God works *ad extra*, outside of the Trinity, this always happens through his "Gift": the eternal conception in God is the basis for all created conception. That is what is meant by the mysterious statement at the moment of creation: "And the Spirit of God moved over the waters." And when the Son takes on flesh in time, this happens through the personified Gift of God, the Holy Ghost. As the eternal Son is begotten by the Father in the eternal Conception, so the Son becomes man in time through the same Conception, the Holy Ghost: "who was conceived by the Holy Ghost". In order for this to happen, however, the Holy Ghost prepares for himself on earth a creature in which he expresses the fact that he is eternally Conception and makes her the created, Immaculate Conception.

> "This eternal, Immaculate Conception (the Holy Ghost) immaculately forms the divine life in the womb of her virginal soul, as the Immaculate Conception. And the virginal womb of her body is reserved for him alone and in him she conceives in time (just as everything material happens in time) the divine life of the God-man as well."[193]

193. BMK, p. 598.

Mary, the Immaculate Conception, is thus the created continuation of the self-giving of Father and Son. This mutual Gift is the Holy Ghost, and in keeping with the eternal will he is accompanied by the created *Immaculata Conceptio* as his spouse, his image, his created extension. This is the eternal divine basis for all her greatness. Thus Mary is the most characteristic revelation of the Holy Ghost. Everything about her is given to him; he can work completely and utterly in her and through her. What she says, he says; what she does, he does in her as its primary cause. Therefore, when someday everything has returned to the life of the Trinity, then Mary remains forever the beloved Gift of Father and Son, the created "face" and the *locus* of the Holy Ghost. Thus Saint John Damascene calls her "the inmost chamber of the Holy Ghost",[194] and *The Akathist Hymn* sings to her, "Hail, place of the God Who is beyond space! Hail, reflection of the divine beauty!"

Yet Mary is also most intimately connected with the Father through the mystery of Filiation (the begetting of the Son). "God the Father imparted to Mary his fruitfulness as far as a mere creature was capable of receiving it, to enable her to bring forth his Son and all of the members of his Mystical Body."[195]

> God the Father gathered all the waters together and called them the seas or *maria*. He gathered all his grace together and called it Mary or *Maria*. The great God has a treasury or storehouse full of riches in which he has enclosed all that is beautiful, resplendent, rare, and precious, even his own Son. This immense treasury is none other than Mary whom the saints call the 'treasury of the Lord'.[196]

194. *Oratio 1 in nativitatem BMV*, in: *Enchiridion Marianum*, *op. cit.* p. 1642.
195. *True Devotion*, paragraph 17, p. 7.
196. *Ibid.*, paragraph 23, p. 9.

By this Saint Louis de Montfort means that Mary is privileged to receive the whole eternal begetting of the Father, "even his only Son", and that she furthermore is entitled to participate in this act of begetting, and therefore in the most intrinsic characteristic of the Father's personhood.

> 'This day have I begotten thee.' So said God the Father and Mary at the same time. He said it in heaven, and she—on earth at Nazareth. Did the Father say this only in heaven? Did he not rather say it in every place where his Son was? Did he not speak his eternal Word, consequently, also in the Virgin's womb, indeed, *into* the Virgin's womb? And didn't Mary bring forth the One who at the moment of her motherly act was likewise begotten in God's bosom? Thus God the Father and Mary begot the same Son at the same moment.[197]

The great bishop and preacher Bossuet says the same:

> Since God decided that the Virgin would give birth in time to him whom he perpetually begets in eternity, He associated her in a certain manner to his eternal begetting. Associating her to his eternal begetting means that God made her the mother of the same son. O Mary, even if I had the intelligence of an angel, an angel of the highest hierarchy, my concepts would be much too imperfect in order to grasp this most perfect union of the Father with you.[198]

Thus the Immaculata enters into the Father's own act of begetting as his perfect image. The Father begets the Son and now involves in this act the mother who, with the Son, can also bring forth all the members of his Mystical Body. Now this begetting is an everlasting one

197. C. Feckes, "Die Gottesmutterschaft", in: P. Sträter, *Maria in der Glaubenswissenschaft* (Paderborn, 1962), p. 60.

198. *2. Predigt am Freitag der Passionswoche*, in: P. Sträter, *op. cit.*, p. 60.

and continues through all eternity. That means for us a perpetual, eternal reception of our being, of our happiness, of our eternity from the everlasting Father and our heavenly mother in the act of begetting the Only-begotten Son.

But what is her relationship then to the eternal Word, whose mother she became in time?

> Jesus Christ, the God-man, true God, the second person of the most Blessed Trinity, is truly her child. She is his true mother. He keeps his fourth commandment and honors his mother. A son never ceases being the son of his mother, and so Jesus will be her son for all eternity, and she will be his mother eternally. He honored her from all eternity and will honor her for all eternity. No one will draw near him, be conformed to him, be saved or sanctified unless he honors her: neither an angel nor a human nor any other being.[199]

Mary will be honored for all eternity as his mother. Whereas the Son responds to his begetting by the Father in eternity, "Abba, Father!" and gives himself unreservedly to him, He says in the same breath, "My mother!" Together with him she exercises royal authority in heaven, the new Eve at the side of the new Adam, the bride of the Lamb at the Redeemer's side. "At your right hand stands the queen.... In gold-woven robes, in many-colored robes she is led to the king..." (Ps 44). "Hail, mother clothed with light, who hast borne the Sun that never sets" (*Akathist*).

When we meditate in the last Glorious mystery on the coronation of Mary in heaven, then that surely concerns her dignity as the Queen of the whole Church Triumphant, of all angels and saints. Yet since the Holy Trinity gives Mary the crown of glory, we can regard this

199. Fragment of his unfinished book on the Immaculata, August 1940, BMK, pp. 600-601.

also as the expression of her eternal and most intimate relationship to the three divine persons: the crown then signifies the glorification of her dignity, the award for her greatness and image and daughter of the Father, as bridal mother of the son, as created personification of the Holy Ghost. One could also interpret this coronation in such a way that through Mary the Holy Trinity acquires the highest praise and glory. Saint Bernard expresses himself in this manner: "From her fullness all have received: the one in bondage—deliverance, the sick—healing, the sorrowful—consolation, the sinner—forgiveness, the righteous—grace, the angel—joy, and finally, the whole Trinity—praise."[200] And Saint Cyril of Alexandria even says: "Through you the Trinity is honored, worshiped, and hallowed."[201] In her is fulfilled the purpose of all created things: to be the praise of the glory of the Triune God.

> Mary is full of the radiance, the representation and the expression of divine glory. God's work, absolutely speaking, God's wondrous work is Mary; never will the like be found. This work, therefore, is full of the Lord's glory, which is poured out upon every pure creature and is most perfectly reflected in Mary. For besides the human nature assumed by the Word, there is no work, no creature in which so much divine praise is reflected as in Mary. For the Lord gained through Mary, through Mary's fullness, praise from the restoration that occurred in heaven, praise from the redemption that took place on earth, praise from the deliverance that occurred in the nether world.... God cannot create anyone greater than she is.[202]

O Immaculata, into what depths you lead your

200. *Sermo de duodecim praerogativis BMV*, in: P. Sträter, *op. cit.*, p. 66.
201. *Homilia 4*, in: *Enchiridion Marianum, op. cit.*, p. 808.
202. Konrad von Sachsen, *Speculum BMV, lect. 7*, in: P. Sträter, *op. cit.*, p. 67.

unworthy child! In the beginning was the Word and the Word was with God and the Word was God. Always there is this endless ocean of divinity. But in this ocean, in God's endless thoughts, there is a point around which everything revolves, to which God is drawn again and again. It is a droplet, a nonentity, infinitely small. And this drop becomes the occasion for God to show his greatness by way of contrast: the Greatest of all decides to become smaller than the "least of all" his works. And without losing his divinity and sanctity, he creates for himself a being in which he can be mirrored as though in his antithesis. And this being is you, dear Lady! God is love, forever! But in your case God becomes love in a special way by giving of himself to the utmost of his capacity. The place, however, in which he can give himself completely and utterly, this place must not offer any resistance, for otherwise God cannot give himself. And this place is you!

Everything else is the consequence of this first *actio Dei* and of this first *reactio creaturae.*

The creation of the world—according to your nature, according to the original, immaculate concept of you, *Immaculata Conceptio*. For the world is what it is only insofar as it has been taken up by divine love, and all creatures are oriented in their intrinsic nature toward the prototype that God has taken completely and utterly to himself, and that is you!

The Redemption of the world—through the coming of the second divine person into you and solely through you.

The sanctification of the world—through the coming of the third divine person into you and solely through you.

The return of the world—as creatures go along with the stream of divine love that is poured out into hearts through you and also returns to God again through you.

And at the end of the world there is God again, the Three in One! And everything has entered into you. you are the heaven, the place, the everlasting dwelling of the Most High. In you we may share in the ocean of love without end: *participes divinae naturae*.

O IMMACULATA!

I adore You, Our Father in heaven, because You have placed Your only-begotten Son in her most-pure womb.

I adore You, Son of God, because You have deigned to descend into her pure womb and become her true, real Son.

I adore You, Holy Ghost, because You have deigned to form the body of God's Son in her immaculate womb.

I adore You, most Holy Trinity, O God in Three Persons, for so divinely exalting the Immaculata. And I will never cease worshiping You every day upon awakening from sleep, in profound humility, with head bowed to the ground, O Triune God, saying three times, "Glory be to the Father and to the Son and to the Holy Ghost, as it was in the beginning, is now and ever shall be, world without end. Amen."

Allow me to praise you, O most Blessed Virgin.

Allow me to praise you at the expense of my strength.

Allow me to live, work, and suffer for you and for you alone, to spend myself and die for you.

Allow me to place the whole world at your feet.

Allow me to contribute to your greater —indeed, to your greatest — possible glorification.

Allow me to offer you such honor as no one has ever yet offered you.
Allow me to be surpassed by others in their zeal for your glorification, so that I may then, as though in a noble contest, promote devotion to you ever more deeply, swiftly, and splendidly, as desired by him who exalted you so ineffably over all other creatures.
In you alone was God glorified incomparably more than in all his saints.
For you God created the world. For you God also called me into being. Whom am I that I should have such good fortune?
O allow me to praise you, O most holy Virgin.[203]

203. St. Maximilian Kolbe, *Rycerz Niepokalanej* 18 (1939), pp. 129-130, BMK, pp. 588-589.

Saint Maximilian Kolbe (1894-1941)